A Case of Bananas

and other
South Sea Trials

By the same author

Tales from a Palm Court
Tales of a Man Called Father

RONNIE KNOX MAWER

A Case of Bananas

and other
South Sea Trials

Illustrations by
TONY DOVER

MICHAEL O'MARA BOOKS LIMITED

NOTE

As a British Judge in the South Pacific,
Ronnie Knox Mawer's circuit stretched north
of Capricorn for three thousand miles, from
Polynesian Tawahi in the west, through
Salu-Salu and Bai Lalevu in central
Micronesia, to Melanesian Tavula in eastern
Oceania. Naturally, in this wide and
colourful judicial parish, the author's more
bizarre adventures have required a little
prudent disguise for both characters
and place names.

First published in 1992 in Great Britain by
Michael O'Mara Books Limited, 9 Lion Yard,
Tremadoc Road, London SW4 7NQ

A CIP catalogue record for this book is available from
the British Library

ISBN 1–85479–165–6

Book designed by Simon Bell

Typeset by Florencetype Limited, Kewstoke, Avon

Printed and bound in Great Britain by
Richard Clay Limited, Bungay, Suffolk

Contents

Chapter One

The Big Red Book

I SUPPOSE IT WAS a turning point in my career. I mean the accident that befell me at the stately pile off Trafalgar Square known as the Royal Empire Society. I was paying a visit to the Library there, boning up on the territory where the Colonial Office was sending me. As a raw recruit in H.M. Overseas Judiciary I was anxious to make a good impression.

It happened while I was rummaging along the dusty shelves in the icy gloom of the Equatorial Section. The sepulchral silence of the Reading Room was broken by a rumble overhead that sounded like an avalanche on a mountain pass. Someone in the gallery above had dislodged a cascade of books. The next minute a particularly large volume struck me on the head, causing the room to spin. For a few seconds I sat down on the floor. When I recovered, the Librarian was examining a thick red book the size of a family Bible.

'Made a nasty dent in the cover I'm afraid,' he complained. He was pointing an accusing forefinger at the sub-title on the spine.

'*Tropical Vices for the British Abroad,*' I read out groggily.

'*Tropical SERvices*', he corrected trying to stub back the torn piece of binding into position.

'My fault entirely,' interjected a tweedy matron smelling of mothballs. 'Such a splendid book too.'

She bent over it reverently.

'What would we all do without the *Army and Navy Stores' Catalogue?*'

She leaned towards me. 'You've got your own copy, of course?'

'Afraid not.'

'You are going abroad though?'

'Yes. Colonial Judiciary.'

'Well, you certainly can't do without this,' she instructed. 'Everybody calls it The Big Red Book. You'd better have a jolly good look at it here and now.'

'Am I allowed to take it home with me?' I asked the Librarian. I was wanting a lie-down in my Bloomsbury lodgings.

'Sorry, no. This is a reference book.'

The Librarian was already busy with paste and scissors, but perhaps he noticed the crestfallen expression on my face.

'Tell you what. I've got a brand-new copy. This'll never do for us now. I'll sell it to you for a pound.'

Back in my bed-sit I opened The Big Red Book. My head was still aching as I tried to figure out the listings at the front. Confectionery, Groceries, Ironmongery, Men's Outfitting, Cabin-Trunks, Sports-Goods, Furnishings, Visiting-Cards, Safari-Equipment – the catalogue seemed endless. I put a cold-water bandage over my bruised forehead, downed a couple of aspirins and carried The Big Red Book to bed.

The sporting section opened with an artist's impression entitled 'Officers Club Out East'. A pukka sahib in pith-helmet and riding-breeches was leaving the pillared steps of the Club while a dutiful syce in a flowing turban held a fine white stallion for him to mount.

Another advertisement read SATISFIED VISITOR
FROM OUR BOMBAY MENSWEAR DEPART-
MENT. The customer in a white mess-jacket and
medal-ribbons stood on the edge of a palm-fringed mar-
quee, about to make his mark on the ballroom floor.
Drifting off to sleep it struck me that, according to The
Big Red Book, I could expect a dashing way of life in the
service of Empire.

Next morning I collected my Letter of Appointment
from Harold Langford-Smith, the Recruitment Officer
at the Colonial Office, known in the Service as Languid
Smith.

'Make sure you stock up at the Army and Navy Stores,
old boy,' were his parting words. 'Remember, you're
going to the very back of beyond.'

'I've got the catalogue already,' I said with some
pride.

'Well, mention my name to Mr Greasby, the Exports
Manager, when you place your order.'

I sped posthaste to the famous emporium at 105
Victoria Street. The entrance hall was draped in Union
Jacks, a centrepiece of clocks showing the time in each
part of the Empire. It was midnight in Hong Kong, eight
in Jamaica, four in Singapore, seven in Lagos, but there
was no mention of Tawahi, my own destination.

A deposit of £5 opened my account and afforded me
an introduction to Mr Greasby.

'Good idea to start with the Wines and Spirits, sir,' he
said. 'Most clients enjoy a little tasting in that particular
department.' From the purple tint of his nose it was
clear that Mr Greasby also enjoyed this exercise.

A creaking lift took us up past the Nelson and
Wellington Reception Rooms. We emerged on the
second floor where Mr Greasby studied the details of my

overseas station on the Order Book.

'We pride ourselves on shipping our bonded liquor to anywhere, however remote,' he assured me. We were now in the palatial Duty-Free Department itself.

'May I recommend,' he said, stopping at the first counter, 'our own special blend of Old Grain Whisky at 142 shillings per half dozen.'

He measured off a tot from a cask standing to hand.

'Quite a kick,' I gasped.

We moved on to another barrel.

'The Heavy Malt,' said Mr Greasby with a flourish. 'Stands up exceptionally to the storms off Cape Cod and keeps its flavour whatever the temperature.'

He drew a generous sample.

'Have you ever met such roundness, sir?'

I blinked.

'And now let me introduce you to our Fine Liqueur Cognac. The High Commissioner for Papua and New Guinea always lays in a couple of dozen for his Christmas entertaining.'

Was it wise to try the High Commissioner's Cognac, I wondered afterwards?

Mr Greasby waved his hand at the gin display.

'Our Plymouth Unsweetened,' he said. 'Especially popular in the Union Club. High Chief Ratu Epili Mokaseseiabe keeps his own special account. Gets through a bottle a week.'

I goggled.

'No more than a taste, thank you,' I said, without much conviction.

Our next port of call was a counter marked Cocktail Bases.

'This is our famous Raffles Sidecar,' he said. 'You could always pop in your own home-grown pineapples or a sprinkling of coconut from your plantation.'

The Big Red Book

Mr Greasby had a rather vague idea of my judicial duties.

'Afraid I'll be desk-bound in a court-room,' I said, foolishly giving way to the Raffles Sidecar.

I was even more misguided to end up with something called the Happy Valley Orange Glow.

'Orange Glow' just about summed up my condition as I accompanied Mr Greasby through the remaining twenty-two departments of the stores. My recollection of that part of the visit was distinctly hazy. I told myself that the sampling had combined disastrously with the blow to my temple of the previous day. Whatever the reason, I seemed to place a wildly haphazard collection of orders. All I could remember was a distinctly firm refusal on my part to visit the Ladies Maternity Section.

A week later I was back in lodgings when the telephone rang. An adenoidal voice came on the line.

'Mr Greasby's Assistant here, sir. Just have to tell you what is owed.'

'Hang on,' I said. 'I'll get my copy of your catalogue.'

I opened up The Big Red Book as the caller began to list the items in a voice like the Vicar reciting the Collect for the Day.

'One Kitchener Water Barrow Extra Strong with Galvanized Steel Tub Hooped Bottom and Solid Square Iron Frame.'

'What was that?'

'One set of Wasp-Traps Adaptable for Locusts,' the caller droned on.

'What on earth are you talking about? I didn't . . .'

'One Rhinoceros-Beetle Foot Spray Bellows. Best Quality Leather.'

'Look here—'

'Four pairs Gold Coast Mangrove Ankle Clogs,' the voice continued relentlessly. 'Complete with Iron Clamps.'

A Case of Bananas

'Is this some sort of joke?' I demanded.

'Six Anglo-Indian Gauze Pullovests with Matching Jaylax Drawers Waist-Unshrinkable.'

A silence fell. I was covered in perspiration from head to foot.

'Is it to late to cancel the order?' I croaked.

'Sorry sir. Already despatched by surface delivery,' came the reply. 'Some of the smaller items will, of course, be in your cabin already.'

The s.s. *Rangitani* sailed from Southampton. I had to admit that, in the Bay of Biscay, Item 14, the Anti-Travel Sickness Belt in Gents Silk, Simple Cheap and Effective, did prove a godsend. And Item 26, the Demon Utility Sponge was useful in the cold salt-water bath on Deck C. However, my Rangoon Cane 'Restawhile' took quite a lot of setting up on the sun-deck. The Quality Steel Tubes for Rapid Assembly did not live up to their description. Helpful passengers extricated me on the first couple of occasions. Eventually, though, the purser came to my assistance and I was able to stretch out for a few moments before the sunset-bugle.

When I landed in Tawahi, I was greeted by a scholarly-looking Indian gentleman with half-moon spectacles and a stern expression. He was wearing a white Nehru-style jacket, heavily starched, with matching leggings. He strode towards me with a brisk squeaking of his highly polished brown shoes.

'Chief Registrar Pandit Raj Sharma,' he introduced himself. 'Here to conduct you to your quarters.'

I was relieved to find someone so evidently in charge.

'An order from the Army and Navy Stores has arrived for you,' he said, making his way through the Customs Office. 'One large item has already been opened under my supervision.'

He seemed to inspect me rather strangely.

'How are you feeling?' he enquired in a concerned tone as we stepped into the government gharry waiting on the quay.

'Perfectly well, thank you,' I replied.

He drew out a small blue bottle from his pocket.

'Smelling salts,' he said. 'My wife's mother finds them most efficacious.' We were trotting along the sea-front bazaar. 'And if you need something stronger, there is the Government pharmacy.'

'Perhaps another time,' I said politely.

'Anyway, the Government doctor lives only in the next compound to yours.'

'Ah – er, very good,' I said, even more bemused.

We drew up at my bungalow. Packing cases stamped Army and Navy Stores were piled up on every side. Mr Sharma seemed to be helping me to the nearest chair.

'I expect you'll be liking to meet the padre,' he said. 'I can deliver a note to the Reverend gentleman on my way back.'

'Surely there's plenty of time for that later,' I said.

With an understanding look Mr Sharma simply indicated a large, already opened, crate.

Beneath the straw I caught a glimpse of veneered oak and two brass handles.

Dropping his eyes tactfully Mr Sharma handed me the Bill of Lading. In Greasby's unsteady hand I read the entry: ONE MANDALAY COMBINED HAND-HEARSE AND BIER. PLEASE HANDLE WITH CARE.

Chapter Two

Our Man in Mosquito Boots

I WAS DOING MY BEST to settle down in the South Seas. Once again, however, I found myself misled by The Big Red Book.

There was no doubting that the illustrations in the catalogue had given me delusions of grandeur. An artist's drawing which was the centrepiece of the travelling equipment section, for instance, showed a District Judge about to tour his domain. The judge was ensconced in a silken howdah on top of a stately elephant, while awaiting instructions below was a turbanned mahout perched astride two giant grey earflaps. By contrast, upon taking my own judicial appointment, I found myself provided with a creature no bigger than a donkey. My feet touched the ground on both sides and only its little tusks indicated that it belonged to the elephant species at all.

'Is your Honour not familiar with the Tawahi Dwarf variety?' inquired Josefa, the Court Orderly.

In a way, I suppose this was a symbol of what was to follow. For my vanity was certainly dashed when I discovered my position in the official pecking order. Of course, it was my first appointment in the Service and I was only a Probationary Judicial Officer, Grade Two. Even so, as I said to Pennington, a friendly District Commissioner, over tiffin at the Club, I hadn't expected to rank in protocol below the Income Tax Supervisor.

'Don't let it get you down, my lad,' said Pennington who was on his fourth chotta peg. 'We've all had to start somewhere.'

'Well, I had thought anyone representing the Crown on the Bench would enjoy a bit more recognition,' I complained. 'Don't expect the Governor even realizes I'm here.'

The DC clamped a hairy arm around my shoulders.

'I'll soon put that right. A word in Miss Massingberd's ear should do the trick.'

'Miss Massingberd?'

'She's the Secretary at Government House. In charge of the Garden Party.'

'Garden Party?'

'Big annual affair. Absolutely *de rigueur* to go to that.'

'That'll be something to look forward to, at least,' I said.

'Wish I felt the same way,' groaned Pennington.

He put down his empty glass.

'Anyway, provided you stand the last round, I'll try to make sure you receive an invitation. As it happens, I'm putting in my three months' stint as Governor's Aide-de-Camp. It's one of the burdens of being an Administrative Officer, I fear.'

Some weeks later, I called on Henry Pickles, the Legal Draftsman, during a court adjournment. He was out. Peering into his well appointed office – on the cool side of Government Buildings – I could not help noticing that he had received his invitation to the Garden Party. Gold-edged, with an impressive Royal Crest at the top, it was proudly displayed on the Doulton water-filter, an amenity which was also a particular privilege of Grade One status. I returned to my own premises feeling uneasy.

'Anything in the mail-box for me?' I inquired of Mr Sharma, the Court Registrar. Mr Sharma's severe gaze, through reading spectacles worn on the tip of his scholarly nose, reminded me all too vividly of my junior housemaster at Grove Park School, Wrexham. The Registrar had my welfare at heart but was evidently critical of my failure to settle into an orderly routine.

'Your dhobi bill is already outstanding for one month's washing,' he remonstrated 'And Yee Joy, the greengrocer, writes to say last week's bananas are not returnable.'

I hurried past him into court, a stuffy little arena with a tin roof and a single creaking fan. I took my place on the 'Bench', a peeling leather chair containing a broken spring repaired with guava twine by the faithful Josefa, my orderly. The regular audience in the Public Gallery – a bamboo enclosure on the rear verandah – pressed forward expectantly. For myself, though, my case list was already acquiring a certain monotony – pig theft, after-hours toddy drinking and the usual summonses against Boomerang Taxis, the local firm whose rickshaw drivers constantly ignored the 5 m.p.h. speed limit on the sea front.

Big Emmy was in the dock once more. The proprietress of the local Hibiscus Nightclub, she had quarrelled with the Government Sanitary Inspector again. He had issued her with another complaint about the lack of hygiene in the dining-room – another bunch of hairpins in the turtle soup-of-the-day. Emmy was more than twice the size and weight of the complainant and had hurled the little Gujerati official into the nearby lagoon. I awarded him a substantial amount of compensation, forfeited her bond and adjourned for the day.

'No letter from Government House,' Mr Sharma reported once more the following morning. He sighed and clicked his tongue. It was this familiar expression of reproval that stung me into action. I nerved myself and, there and then, rang up the Governor's Private Secretary herself.

'What can I do for you?' she demanded, in a distinctly frosty tone.

By now I had actually encountered Ursula Massingberd. On the Gymkhana tennis courts. The score had been 6-love, 6–1, 6-love, in her favour.

'Sorry to bother you, Miss Massingberd,' I began. There was a silence. 'But I don't seem to have been asked to the Garden Party,' I went on. There was another pause. I could hear the rustle of impatiently turned pages, as she checked her list.

'We've had to cut back wherever possible this year,' she told me sharply. 'There's a contingent of visiting VIPs from New Zealand, with wives. So I had to refuse Pennington's request on your behalf.'

On the following afternoon I was still in low spirits over this setback. And doing pretty badly on the beginners court at the Gymkhana Club.

'Ah, there you are!' called a familiar voice from the touch-line. It was Miss Massingberd again, twanging her racket in an intimidating sort of way.

'I'm nowhere up to your standard,' I began, thinking she had been landed with me as her partner in the Round-Robin Tournament.

'No, no,' she corrected. 'It's about the Garden Party. I may be able to get you an invitation after all.' She performed a muscular knees-bend. 'Provided,' she went on, 'you're willing to deputize as Aide-de-Camp.'

Big Emmy was in the dock once more

Our Man in Mosquito Boots

I listened in dismay while she explained that Pennington had been suddenly laid low with a bout of malaria.

'Most unexpected,' she added. 'JS is never ill.'

That was obvious. I had already seen Pennington in action on the polo ground. Not that I played, of course, but it was on my way to the British Council Library. He was a huge man, about eighteen stone. I had watched him run through a string of fresh polo ponies in the course of a few chukkas.

'What on earth will I do for a uniform?' I asked Miss Massingberd. 'You're surely not expecting me to wear Pennington's!'

'I don't see why not,' she said. 'Obviously, it'll need taking in here and there. But Kasimbo is a dab hand at that sort of thing. He's been the valet at GH for nearly half-a-century, you know.'

I did not want to fall out with the Establishment at that stage of my career. Reluctantly, I fell in with her suggestion.

There was a slight problem with Kasimbo. His eyesight was clearly failing. But there was no point in my being fussy. Even so, the folds in Pennington's tacked-up uniform made for a good deal of extra discomfort, especially as we were now right into the hot season.

At least Ursula Massingberd was level with me over Pennington's mosquito boots.

'I know they're a couple of sizes too big,' she agreed. 'You'll just have to tread carefully, that's all.'

The great day dawned under heavy monsoonal cloud. It took me some time to get ready, even with the help of Mr Sharma. 'Your bicycle rickshaw's been waiting for over half an hour,' he scolded.

Upon drawing up at the pillared entrance to

'Individual portrait, sir?'

Our Man in Mosquito Boots

Government House it was my fault that Pennington's ceremonial sword had to be abandoned. Both the rickshaw driver and I wrestled hard to extricate the scabbard from the rattan-seat. To no avail.

This initial mishap unquestionably sapped my confidence, especially when I saw the awesome figure of the Governor himself, pacing to and fro on the terrace in his vice-regal plumes. Miss Massingberd was at his side.

'Reporting for duty, Sir,' I called out.

The expression on His Excellency's face was one of consternation as I floundered up the steps in Pennington's seven-league mosquito boots.

'Er – welcome to the Colony, Knox Mawer,' he said. He shook me by the hand, accidentally removing one of Pennington's dress-gloves. 'Appreciate your stepping into the breach.'

Miss Massingberd moved forward, brandishing a large parasol, and whispered something in his ear.

'Better stand him behind the tea-urns,' His Excellency replied in an under-tone.

The first guests were already lining up to be introduced on the lawn. At Miss Massingberd's command, I hastened through the shrubbery towards the marquee where I was to lend a hand with the refreshment arrangements.

'With or without lemon, Madam?' I enquired of the Bishop of the Colony. The steam from the tea-urn had clouded my spectacles and I suppose I was momentarily confused by his wide-brimmed clerical hat.

There was a cracking sound from outside. The wind was getting up, billowing the purdah tent at the far end of the lawn. High time those guy ropes were slackened, I decided, hurrying across.

The tent was provided for the wives of the Indian guests. Unfortunately, the re-fastening of the side-flaps involved me in a considerable struggle. Shrill cries of feminine alarm broke out. At the same moment the Governor's party was moving past towards the saluting base.

'For heaven's sake,' I heard His Excellency explode. 'Does he have to behave like a Peeping Tom!'

The next moment Miss Massingberd had hooked me into line with the handle of her parasol. An official photograph was about to be taken, it seemed.

'Everybody look happy,' called a hoarse voice from the oleander bushes. A.J. HAK KING OF THE KODAK read the placard hanging from the photographic tripod set up in a corner of the shrubbery. I adjusted Pennington's size 8 pith-helmet to reveal a little more of my face.

'Not to move,' commanded Mr Hak, retreating under his canopy.

There was a sudden explosion and a great deal of smoke. The saturnine features of Mr Hak reappeared like the demon in a pantomime.

'Hold horses please,' he advised. 'Flash-bang's gone for the Burton.' Ever watchful for trouble, the Commissioner of Police hurried the Vice-regal party away. I found myself alone with Mr Hak.

'Individual portrait, Sir, special offer?' he suggested.

He looked me up and down.

'Just head and shoulders maybe?'

Before I could stop him, he was snapping away with a Box Brownie, much to the entertainment of the onlookers. From the lower lawn came the sound of drums. It was high time I rejoined the Governor's entourage.

A colourful column of native levies, resplendent in turbans of red, white and blue, were parading under the palm trees. I took my place behind the Governor's chair.

'Very impressive, Sir, these tribal customs,' I ventured.

The plumes of His Excellency's head-dress quivered. He continued to look straight ahead.

'They happen to be Beating the Retreat,' he said. 'And I'm beginning to wish you'd do the same!'

In spite of these discouragements, I was determined to see the job through to the end. I came to attention for the Last Post and made my salute upon the Lowering of the Flag. An ominous black cloud blotted out the tropical sunset as I returned home and struggled out of my borrowed plumage.

When I called upon Pennington later that evening to return his outfit, he was drinking a large brandy and seemed perfectly fit again.

'Good of you to step into my shoes,' he said.

'Even better to step out of them,' I answered with feeling.

Chapter Three

Looking after the Master

'YOU'RE an arty young bastard!'
It was Craig Peterson, the bluff Australian
Public Relations Officer on the line.

'So looking after this flaming Noël Coward should be
right up your street.'

After a pretty shaky start to my new life abroad I
could hardly believe my luck. I had always been a keen
member of the Lincolns Inn Young Thespians, and the
thought of meeting one of my great theatrical idols
seemed too good to be true.

'The joker's not arriving until February,' Craig added.
'I'll keep you posted.'

About three weeks later Mr Sharma interrupted me on
the Bench. I was dealing with the regular morning
round-up of intoxicated beachcombers and ladies of the
town.

'A Mr Knowle on the telephone,' he said.

I'd already made an appointment with Jack Knowle,
the Maintenance Foreman at the Public Works
Department, to see to a blocked septic tank at my
bungalow.

'Tell him I'm expecting him first thing tomorrow
morning with his pumping equipment,' I said.

Looking after the Master

A few moments later, the Registrar tapped me on the shoulder again.

'Mr Knowle insists on speaking to you,' he said.

I strode out to the office and snatched up the receiver.

'Don't seem to have brought my pumping equipment with me, dear boy,' said the voice on the other end. 'But I have a note here at the hotel to telephone you.'

The clipped accent and burst of staccato laughter which followed could only belong to one person.

'Mr Coward!' I stammered.

'Noël, please,' he corrected.

'Dreadfully sorry . . . clerk got the wrong name . . . no idea you'd actually arrived . . .'

He cut me short. 'Pop round for a drink at six,' he said, and put down the phone.

Court proceedings were over by five, giving me time to shower and slip into my recently acquired Club blazer. A touch of talcum powder helped to disguise the scorch mark on the lapel, left by Mattie Tonga, the Fijian housekeeper, in her over-enthusiastic application of the charcoal-iron. The paisley cravat from Debenhams – a Christmas present from Aunt Sylvia – added to what I hoped was the final touch of casual sophistication.

The clock on Government Buildings was chiming at six as I drove down Victoria Parade to the Grand Pacific Hotel. It was the height of the hot season and somehow appropriate, I thought, that a clap of thunder and flash of forked lightning should accompany my first glimpse of the great man. A slim, tanned figure, in blue slacks and matching shirt, he was leaning nonchalantly against the balcony, unperturbed by the weather effects off-stage.

As we shook hands the clouds opened.

'So kind of you to invite me for a sundowner,' I said,

above the noise of the rain.

'Not too sure about the sun,' he replied, 'but downing a large gin should be simple.'

Inside the main reception room a solitary punkah churned the air above a sea of deserted tables. On top of the bar a Fijian waiter lay curled up fast asleep. He was quickly in action, however, and produced his own version of the manhattan ordered by Noël.

'Cannibal cocktail for two,' he beamed, handing us each a foaming green concoction.

'We're rather proud of our Grand Pacific Hotel,' I remarked.

There was a pause while Noël looked around.

'Pacific undoubtedly. Hotel possibly. Grand never.'

'Somerset Maugham liked it here,' I said, a touch on the defensive.

There came a fresh downpour on the glass roof overhead.

'I suppose it's where Willie got the idea for that gloomy little story of his,' Noël replied.

'*Rain?*' I put in knowledgeably.

'*Rain,*' he said. His voice had a dying fall and I hastily ordered another round.

'How's the New York show going?' I ventured.

Noël wasn't anxious to pursue this particular topic and we moved on to discuss plans for the next day.

'Mustn't budge an inch,' he warned, 'until I've signed The Book.'

It was colonial etiquette to acknowledge the Queen's Representative by signing His Excellency's Visitors' Book.

Another cloud burst over the mangrove swamp.

'Better turn in with Jane,' Noël announced briskly.

I tried not to look inquisitive.

'Never travel anywhere without Miss Austen.'

Before leaving the bar he brought out an unopened pack of expensive cigarettes. 'Yield not to temptation,' he said, presenting them to the delighted barman.

'Promised Ed Biggs to give up smoking entirely – my Chicago doctor – forever prophesying doom.'

Ten o'clock next morning saw me on duty again. Noël came bounding towards the car. He was now in splendid form – unlike my decrepit Volkswagen, the door of which refused to open. Exactly the same thing had happened the week before when I offered the Chief Justice a lift. Sir Neville had pranced off in a huff. Noël simply folded himself into the other side without demur.

It was less than a mile to Government House. As we turned into the gates, I had problems with the clutch.

'Do take care,' said Noël's voice in my ear, as he was jerked forward against the driving seat. 'You have a very precious cargo.'

The Visitors' Book was kept in a kind of sentry box at the foot of GH steps. It lay open at the current page of signatures, smudged with rain.

'Time to turn over a new leaf,' Noël announced. With a twirl of his gold fountain pen he added the two famous dots above the e of Noël.

'Since we're here, might as well say hello to the Governor,' I heard him say as he darted up the Vice-regal steps. Just ahead I glimpsed the figure of His Excellency peering out from the verandah.

'Been admiring Your Excellency's little domain,' said Noël. 'Perfectly charming now the weather's cleared a bit.' He waved his arm at the still dripping palms. From the misty lawns below arose a chorus of frog-like amphibians.

'These toads,' said Noël, nodding in their direction,

'don't they stop you sleeping? Found them positively deafening last night. Croaking away like old bishops at The Athenaeum.'

There was a discreet cough from inside the Governor's sanctuary. Through the open door I thought I recognized the purple vestement and white collar of his lordship, the Bishop of Polynesia. It was obviously time to go. As we drove away, I explained to Noël that I was due to hold court on the offshore island of Lovaka that afternoon.

'Why can't I come and see you in action?' he said with an avuncular beam. 'British justice "neath wig and topee". Should be jolly.'

On our way to the Lovaka boat, we dropped in for lunch at Mr Bhicajee Cowasjee's restaurant in Marine Parade. The proprietor himself shuffled forward with dhal soup and onion bajees.

'Here we are killing no live thing,' he insisted. 'It is against our religion.'

'Pity,' Noël observed, brushing aside a large cockroach which had joined us at the table.

From the café we drove to the wharf. A trim white craft, gleaming with polished brass, was moored at the foot of the jetty. Noël was halfway aboard before I had to disillusion him.

'That's the Government House yacht,' I explained. 'This is ours, I'm afraid.' I led him towards the battered ferry-boat alongside. Diesel smoke was already pouring from the engine-house.

The deck was crammed with island passengers and their baggage – rolled mats, baskets of clothes, cooking pots and chickens. As we stepped aboard, my six-foot Polynesian constable presented himself with a smart salute.

'This is Josefa, the Court Orderly,' I said. At that

moment the boat began to move. Noël was intrigued by Josefa's traditional uniform, especially the white kilt with its serrated edge.

'What do you call it?' he asked.

'Sulu,' said Josefa proudly.

'With such a sweet little pointed hemline!' exclaimed Noël. 'Just like the elves in *Where the Rainbow Ends*.'

Always eager to improve his English, Josefa turned to me.

'What is elves?' he asked.

I thought quickly.

'Powerful spirits,' I answered. 'Working strong magic.'

From that moment on, as far as the police orderly was concerned, the visitor could do no wrong.

Enthusiastically, Josefa drew him to the rail to point out various landmarks on the horizon. Soon he was deep into his repertoire of legend. For the next hour, familiar snatches were carried to me on the breeze: '. . . sacred whale . . . great shark-god . . . 500 virgins swim out to meet the chief's war-canoe . . . on Lovaka island feasting and dancing all night long . . .'.

'Can't wait to get to this place Lovaka,' said Noël, 'sounds like a traveller's dream.'

'Things have changed since tribal times,' I murmured.

We were rounding the headland and, even as I spoke, two giant billboards loomed up to greet us. 'Mackenzie Brothers Pineapple Cannery' announced the first. The other was in Japanese and showed a brightly coloured picture of a tin of tuna fish. The tuna factory itself, a huge expanse of corrugated iron, glinted in the sun. Along the waterfront stretched a row of shanty-town bars and curry shops.

As we bumped against the jetty, we were deafened by

a loud screeching sound. A string of grimy waggons, piled high with dried coconuts for the copra market, rattled down the iron track on the quay.

'Rather like arriving at Crewe in a heatwave,' said Noël faintly. But worse lay ahead.

'So this is Palm Court,' was Noël's only comment as I led him into the tiny concrete building behind the Chinese take-away in which I officiated. A ragged Union Jack hung limply over the entrance. Noël collapsed into a canvas chair alongside the rickety bamboo bench.

'And I pictured you dispensing justice by some sleepy lagoon,' he sighed.

'Well, some of the cases are fairly picturesque,' I said, as Mr Sharma came up with the cause-list in his hand.

'What have you got for us today?' I enquired hopefully.

'Collision between tricycle taxi and ox-cart,' he replied 'and one non-payment of banana export tax.'

My heart sank.

A few beachcombers drifted in to listen at the back. As the proceedings droned on, the humidity began to climb alarmingly and I signalled for Mr Sharma to turn on the fan. He shook his head.

'No power.'

'No power?'

'Yesterday, the Nadi Rugby Finals were played here in Lovaka.' His tone was severe.

'And so?'

'Afterwards, the teams got very drunk. Epeli Mauru, the scrum-half, threw a cane knife at Mosese Tarawa, the front row forward. Big flash resulted in the overhead cable. Electricity finished everywhere.'

There was a pause while he unlocked a tin box labelled Exhibit A and solemnly produced a broken lavatory chain.

Looking after the Master

'Players also did great damage to the gentlemen's public convenience,' he complained.

'Time for an adjournment, maybe,' I said to Noël.

Under a solitary banyan tree in the compound I produced a thermos flask of cold tea. Mattie had packed two pilchard sandwiches which were leaking a little in the heat. Noël patted me on the shoulder.

'Think I'll try the Club for a quick martini. Josefa tells me the planters have a place of their own around the corner.'

It must have been 4 p.m. when I finished work and went to collect the visitor. I found him entertaining a couple of elderly remittance men in old khaki shorts and plimsolls.

'They've been introducing me to Dragon whisky,' he said gaily.

I peered at what looked like a very small dead lizard at the bottom of an empty bottle on the table.

'Crocodile gin is better,' said one of the old-timers. 'But we've run out.'

'I'm afraid we are expected back,' I explained.

Noël was reluctant to leave.

'Where do we have to be?' he asked.

'The Ladies Drama Circle has laid on a reception for you in the church-hall,' I said. 'Hope that's in order.'

Noël's expression was enigmatic.

The journey back proved uneventful except for the panama. I was a moment too late to retrieve it from one of the pigs on board, but Noël was very nice about it.

'May I take a photograph?' I asked, as we went ashore. 'Before the light goes?'

He posed for me, obligingly, hands in pockets, against the sunset. In my excitement my old Box Brownie slipped a little as I took the snap, the last on the reel, alas.

A Case of Bananas

We found the long wooden hut next to the Anglican Church buzzing with activity. Mrs Irene Campbell and her helpers had been extremely busy. Paper chains and streamers with sprays of red hibiscus adorned the walls. A large trestle table was piled high with Antipodean home cooking.

'Try the Maori Mouthfulls,' the Vice-President urged Noël, holding out a plate of sponge slices decorated with miniature chocolate boomerangs.

When the tea had been dispensed from a steaming urn in the corner, Mrs Campbell moved ominously across to the upright piano. The lid was raised. Noël was led to it like a lamb to the slaughter, and dutifully sang for his supper.

'Alice is at It Again' was not perhaps the happiest choice. The President decided to help out.

'I prefer your romantic numbers, Mr Coward,' said Mrs Campbell. She edged Noël to the far end of the piano stool, and launched into the opening bars of 'We'll Gather Lilacs'. It took a long half hour for the Ivor Novello repertoire to be exhausted, at which point Noël pleaded a migraine.

'Social life in the South Pacific has its limits,' he observed. He mopped his brow with a yellow silk handkerchief as we limped back to the hotel.

'What do you do in your spare time?'

I confessed that I went in for a spot of writing.

'Anything in print?'

'Just a couple of small pieces,' I said, then, plucking up courage, 'I'll dig one out before I collect you tomorrow.'

Next morning Noël was scheduled to fly on to Tahiti.

'Don't forget to look me up when you're in England, dear boy,' were his final words, as I dropped him at Nadi airport. I had a feeling he said this a good many times on his travels, but I was pretty elated all the same. My only disappointment came upon returning to the car. In the haste of his departure Noël had inadvertently left behind on the seat the inscribed copy of my article, 'Native Funeral Rites and the Law of Bequests in Eastern Polynesia'.

It was the last I saw of the great man. Some time later I happened to be browsing along the shelf of the British Council Library. In the biography section I came across Noël Coward's Diaries. With a beating heart I pulled down the volume. There was bound to be mention of his trip to the South Pacific and our experiences together. I looked up the index – first under K then under M. No luck. Perhaps that was too much to expect. What about the heading Nadi? Yes, there it was. Pages 489–500. I eagerly turned them up. The entry began three-quarters of the way down on page 498. 'February 28 – arrived Monday morning five o'clock Nadi time . . . vile road . . . typical going-to-seed British . . .'

It was not altogether an encouraging start but I pressed on eagerly to the continuation of the sentence on the opposite page.

'The view of Tahiti is exquisite,' I read. What on earth? I glanced up at the page number. It was *501*. I could hardly believe my eyes. THE VITAL PAGE WAS MISSING.

I seized the book by the spine and shook it furiously, to no avail. At this point, I admit, I lost control. I plunged across to Isbel Hak, the librarian, and banged the volume down in front of her.

'Perfectly disgraceful,' I shouted. All heads turned towards me. 'Why on earth do you allow books to get into this state?'

The librarian drew herself up behind the counter.

'Pages often go missing,' she snapped. 'Termites are eating the binding glue.'

I took a deep breath. There was no point in continuing this undignified altercation.

'I shall write to the Head of the British Council,' were my final words.

I returned to the bungalow in search of a strong whisky. At least I had my own souvenirs. Putting down the glass I rummaged in my safari trunk. I hadn't looked through my scrapbook for some time. Yes. There were the precious mementoes! The note scribbled in Noël's own hand, 'Grateful if you would buy me a couple of airmail stamps.' And, pasted alongside, a slightly blurred photograph taken at sunset of Noël Coward's legs.

Chapter Four

That Old Black Magic

IT ALL BEGAN with an unhappy confrontation in Chambers. For the second time that year Constable Josefa had got one of Lady Chumley's girl guides into the family way.

'I've had Lady C. on the phone from Government House, for nearly an hour,' I told him severely. 'She's particularly upset as its one of her best girls – patrol-leader of the Kukuburu Pack!'

I took another indigestion tablet.

'She somehow or other blames me. Says there's a distinct lack of moral discipline in the Judicial Department.'

'Very sorry, sir,' said Josefa, 'very, very sorry. But in my defence, sir, this girl already has two babies adopted by her grandmother.'

'It's the principle that matters,' I said. 'Mr Registrar Sharma insists that I boot you out this time.'

Josefa folded the Notice of Dismissal into the pocket of his flowered bula shirt.

'Just our bad luck, sir,' he said, departing with a rueful salaam.

Two days later Mr Sharma hurried in to see me. He was polishing his spectacles meticulously, always a sign of crisis.

A Case of Bananas

'Josefa's uncle has been sitting under the sacred ivi tree,' he announced.

'Has he, indeed,' I murmured. My mind was preoccupied with a case of pig theft which I had just adjourned in order to consult the decision of the House of Lords in Blandings Pork Butchery *v.* The Royal Agricultural Society 1934, All England Report, pages 142–73.

'Using clay,' Mr Sharma continued, 'this man was making an Image.'

'What of it?' I sighed.

'It was necessary to remove it from him,' continued Mr Sharma, 'perhaps too late, though. I'm afraid the Image is representing Your Honour.' He held out a figure of a manikin with enormous ears, a long pointed head and stick-like legs. If this was meant to be a likeness of me it was, in my opinion, a crude and exaggerated piece of workmanship.

'What on earth are these?' I demanded, pointing to three fish bones stuck through the centre of the Image. Mr Sharma looked grave.

'This means the uncle has made a spell so that bad things may happen to you. Three bad things in this particular type of spell.'

'And why should he do this?' I asked patiently.

'Because you were the one who actually told his nephew to go. He thinks he can make you change your mind.'

'Does he indeed!'

With some distaste I dropped the Image into my out-tray.

'Josefa's uncle is a most powerful witch doctor,' responded Mr Sharma. 'This is not just a matter of island superstition.'

'Nonsense,' I said, anxious to get back into Court and continue with the litigation of the day.

30

That Old Black Magic

In my absence the complainant in the trial had fallen asleep on the bamboo witness-stand.

'Wake up please,' I told him, 'and kindly pay attention to what I'm going to say.'

He nodded drowsily.

'The facts, as I understand them, are these. The defendant is your neighbour. He keeps pigs. So do you. So does everyone else on the island. You swear he's thieved one of your animals. It will be necessary for you to identify features peculiar to the allegedly stolen pig.'

'What the court is saying,' translated Mr Sharma, 'is that it will be necessary to visit the Government Pig Compound and hold an identification parade of the sequestered animals.'

Still in my court dress, I led the procession along the narrow track through the village. The local people liked to see the dignity of the law in action and a large number of them accompanied us to the Compound under the palm trees. Leaning over the rails, the complainant pointed to a particularly large, noisy sow. 'That one, sir, that is the stolen pig.'

'How can you be sure?' I asked.

'She has four warts,' was the reply. 'Here, upon her belly.'

As I leaned forward to confirm this testimony the animal stood up on her hind legs to greet me. Somehow or other her right trotter became entangled with a loose strand of my wig. The next moment, the headpiece (110 guineas, Ede & Ravenscroft, Chancery Lane) was jerked into the trough by my feet. Before I could intervene the wretched creature had snatched it out of the pineapple husks and was gobbling it down with apparent enjoyment. After a moment's reflection I decided that to charge the offender with gross contempt of court would be counterproductive. Heaven knows what would have

31

been the outcome.

'Case proved,' I declared firmly before returning to my seat of justice. There was no time to brood upon this expensive mishap.

'You have to attend an important briefing by Chief Justice Sir Neville Gawsby,' the Registrar reminded me. Within five minutes I had changed into a fresh wing-collar and was bowling along in a bicycle rickshaw for my appointment with the Chief Justice.

Just as I was rounding the bend in Victoria Parade the hub flew off the wheel, spinning me over the breakwater wall. Luckily the tide was out and the rickshaw driver soon fixed me up with a barkcloth sling for my left elbow which had taken a bit of a knock. Mr Sharma arrived with relief transport for me to continue my journey. 'Don't feel quite up to a conference with the CJ,' I told him.

He telephoned apologies to Sir Neville on my behalf, and I returned to Chambers. By this time I was limping a little from a bruise at the back of my left thigh. 'In view of the judge's accident,' the Registrar told Josefa, 'everybody in the case is to be sent away.'

'I see no reason why I should not resume the sitting,' I rejoined. 'Or perhaps I should say the standing.'

At least my sense of humour had not deserted me, but the joke fell flat. Mr Sharma merely repeated his direction to my Police Orderly and turned to other work.

'This has just arrived,' he said, handing me a brown-paper parcel from the afternoon mail. My spirits rose. It contained the proof of the latest paper contributed by me to the *Polynesian Society Journal* on 'The Concept of Tort in the Nacademos Atolls of Western Polynesia'. With mounting excitement I took the manuscript into the outside convenience for perusal. I suppose it was the problem of the sling which caused me to lose the heavy

That Old Black Magic

folio down the septic tank. What made it particularly distressing was the fact that it was my only copy.

'Best to call it a day,' I decided, after this setback.

On my way back to my bungalow, I decided to call in at the HQ of the Overlau Local History Society. Perhaps I ought to take this business of Polynesian magic a little more seriously. Browsing through the shelves I eventually alighted upon Dr Arnold Schreinkopf's *Treatise on Tribal Folklore*. 'When a spell has been cast, the victim will experience a number of accidents which seem to be totally unconnected,' he had written. 'At this stage it is wise to look out for signs of the witch-doctor's activities in the home.'

Back in my quarters I carefully searched the likely points for sorcery noted by the learned doctor. I looked under the mat by the door. No twisted coconut fronds were to be found. Nor in my bedroom did I discover any sign of the black-spotted Papuan cowrie shell suspended under my charpoy.

With a sigh of relief I poured out an evening sun-downer and resumed my weekly letter to Aunt Sylvia in Berkhamsted. I had intended to enclose a snap taken by Mr Sharma of myself opening the current Assize. Unfortunately, someone had now ruined the print by inserting a large boma-thorn through my forehead. It was not difficult to guess who that someone might be.

'I really can't allow this to go on,' I told Mr Sharma next morning, 'childish as it may be.' Mr Sharma blew his nose solemnly.

'Fate has stepped in,' he announced.

'Fate?'

'Yes, indeed. Josefa's uncle passed away in the night. He was of very great age.'

We decided to reinstate Josefa and he was on duty as

usual the following day.

'It was not my doing, sir, that brought my uncle into this,' he explained.

'I'm sure not,' I assured him. 'Just make sure that you keep to the straight and narrow in your personal life from now on. This is your last chance to make good.'

My own chance to make good was something that seemed to be eluding me. A copy of Sir Neville Gawsby's Annual Report had just landed on my desk. 'Since this Memorandum, which I have prepared for the Colonial Office, contains adverse comments upon your showing in the Service,' it read, 'I am required to draw your attention to certain outstanding criticisms. These at present preclude you from further advancement. In outline I have drawn attention to the following defects.' I read on: 'In the first place . . . curious absence of judicial decisiveness . . . over-involvement in local custom . . . marked lack of confidence on official occasions such as Viceregal Garden Party . . .' The whole list made painful reading.

I considered that my Chief Justice was being decidedly unfair.

I still had his disappointing words in mind when I paid a visit to the Occupational Therapy Unit at the Island Girls Reformatory. While watching the art class at work I idly handled a lump of plasticene. Without thinking I must have slipped it into my pocket. Back in my study that evening, after consuming rather more than my usual number of whiskies, I brought out the plasticene and found myself modelling a robust figure that strongly resembled Sir Neville Gawsby. Suddenly, all my bottled-up resentment exploded. Seizing a rusty paper clip from the tray in front of me I thrust it into Sir Neville's stomach. It was an unaccountable action upon my part, although somehow I felt better for it.

Shortly before Christmas Sir Neville returned to the UK for six months' leave. His deputy proved an altogether more sympathetic Head of Department. 'You will be pleased to learn that I have formally approved your upgrading,' he announced on the first working day of the New Year. I thanked him warmly and was just about to leave his Chambers when he picked up a letter with a London postmark. 'Seems Sir Neville was taken suddenly ill with violent abdominal pain,' he murmured. 'Happened at the Commonwealth Law Conference.'

I turned away, hoping to spare the Deputy my guilty flush. Why had I ever allowed myself – a Western man – to dabble in the Polynesian occult! My heart began to pound.

'Is Sir Neville's condition serious?' I ventured.

'Fortunately not,' came the reply. 'Just an appendicitis.' He picked up the letter. 'Says here he'll be back in the Pacific by Easter. Fit as a flea.'

I was relieved, of course. But there was no ignoring the fact that, as with mosquitoes, I was painfully susceptible to the bite of the tropical flea.

Chapter Five

Trouble with the Padre

I HAVE TO ADMIT that my mind was elsewhere at the time. Constable Josefa was robing me, as usual, for my afternoon session on the Bench. Unfortunately, during the luncheon adjournment, a family of monkeys had occupied the Public Gallery and I was debating how to evict them. I was startled out of my reverie, however, by an indignant voice from the door of the verandah.

'Knox Mawer! Are you in the habit of wearing stolen clothing?'

With an uneasy start I recognized the querulous tones of my neighbour, Canon Arthur Stubbs, of the Anglican Church Mission. The next moment the Canon himself appeared, his purple face bulging.

'What on earth do you mean?' I enquired.

Glancing down I was surprised to discover myself arrayed not in my familiar judge's gown but in a scarlet cassock embroidered with gold lilies.

I turned to Josefa. He was busy unwrapping what looked like an ecclesiastical mitre, evidently impressed with these new designs in judicial regalia.

'What is all this?' I asked him.

'Mail from London, my lord,' he replied. 'Special delivery by first-class canoe.'

Then the explanation dawned on me. This was not the

first time there had been a mix-up in postal deliveries between the Court house and the Church Mission next door.

'Our postmaster-general here is a little beyond retirement age,' I told Canon Stubbs. 'Poor old Samuela Bale Nailevu is eighty-five next year.'

The Canon, a newcomer to this island, received my explanation with a marked lack of Christian warmth. In fact, he seemed to have started a war with me right from the word go. He had, of course, a strong military background, having been Chaplain to the Royal Corps of Military Police for fifteen years. And certainly the curl of his huge ginger moustache, above his gleaming clerical collar, suggested an aggressive temperament. Even so, I had not expected the outburst which took place on the morning of the next Quarter Sessions.

The first defendant in the list had been one Tulele Hawai, charged with a disorderly breach of the peace. Tulele was the Church Verger and the Canon himself had initiated the proceedings against him. Apparently the Verger had celebrated his sixtieth birthday party in the Vestry. The celebrations must have gone with a swing because Canon Stubbs had subsequently discovered a lady's grass-skirt abandoned behind the organ-loft.

'A gross act of sacrilege,' according to the Canon.

After two hours of court-room debate he insisted that I refer to the Ecclesiastical Desecration Order-in-Council of 1672.

'But that was a piece of legislation solely aimed at the barbaric ravages of Cromwell's army,' I pointed out, 'and totally irrelevant.'

With some difficulty I persuaded the Canon to resume his place on the large wicker chair set up for him in the front row.

A Case of Bananas

'A conditional discharge is appropriate here,' I announced.

'Kid-glove treatment,' complained Canon Stubbs as he stormed out of the court-room.

A few days later an opportunity arose for me to bury the hatchet. I accepted the Canon's invitation to address the Mandravatu Mothers Union upon the Law relating to Bastardy Indictments. Then, as luck would have it, I failed to keep the appointment, having fallen asleep in the bath with what, I suppose, was my fourth sundowner in my hand – rum and brandy spiked with chillies.

Nor were relations improved by an unhappy incident during the subsequent Assize. I was closing the final summing-up of the day with my customary words of advice to the jury.

'Reach your verdict solely on the evidence,' I told them. 'Allow no extraneous considerations to distract you.'

As I spoke, my own line of thought was disrupted by a blow on the back of the neck. An unripe pineapple rolled to a stop by my feet. Through a gap in the hurricane shutter, I sighted a noisy group of choirboys on the Mission playground. I scribbled a sharp note of complaint.

'Hand this to Canon Stubbs immediately,' I directed Josefa.

Ten minutes later I was obliged to retract my accusation. Apparently, the missile had been thrown by one of the two warders practising basketball outside. There was nothing for it but to send the Canon a note of apology.

My worst blunder, meanwhile, was to invite Canon Stubbs to the quarterly meeting of the Prisoners Welfare

Association. From beginning to end his role was thoroughly destructive. He vetoed my suggestion for an evening of Lake District slides (taken by me on my last home leave) with a rudeness that was quite noticeable.

'Vigorous activity is what these chaps need,' he thundered. 'Bell-ringing, for instance.'

He pointed through the window of my Chambers towards the wooden belfry of his church. It was common knowledge that the Reverend James Brown, the first missionary on the island, had installed a peal of bells there. Just before the islanders had eaten him in 1867.

'Superbly cast by Arkensalls of Birmingham, but seldom used,' the Canon boomed. 'Not since the last hurricane warning, I'm told.'

He rounded upon me.

'Send me your five beefiest offenders,' he insisted. 'I'll have them ringing a triple grandsire for evensong before you can say Jack Robinson.'

'Damn fool' was what I wanted to say in response to this bizarre suggestion. But I did not want to cross swords yet again with Canon Stubbs. Dubiously, I agreed to put it on the agenda for our next quarterly meeting. To my extreme irritation, however, the Canon blatantly stole a march upon me.

It happened in October, the start of the Hilary Sessions, and always the busiest time in my legal calendar. I was trying a rather complex domestic matter in which Mrs Ramraka had been charged by her son-in-law, Dr Naidu, with eavesdropping at Common Law.

'She is listening at the keyhole to medical conversations which are strictly private,' complained Dr Naidu, the island gynaecologist. As he spoke, a thunderous crescendo of bells shattered the orderly tenor of the proceedings.

A Case of Bananas

'We'll need to have those shutters closed,' I said to Mr Sharma.

This had little effect on the appalling noise pouring in from the Mission Church next door. I dispatched the Registrar to investigate, before turning back to the case in hand.

'What my patients tell me is confidential,' continued Dr Naidu, 'but my mother-in-law has no respect for professional etiquette.'

'Ety Ket!' snorted Mrs Ramraka, an ample matron with a diamond in her nose. 'Hanky panky is what he is up to.'

She snatched her sari back over her massive shoulders.

'My duty is to protect my daughter.' She lowered her voice to a scandalized whisper. 'I blush to tell your lordship all the naughty things I overhear.'

Another peal crashed out.

'You'll have to speak up, Madam,' I was saying – at which point we were interrupted by the return of Mr Registrar Sharma. From his report I gathered that the Canon had assembled a makeshift crew of delinquents and commenced rehearsals without even the courtesy of a by-your-leave.

'This is outrageous,' I exclaimed, flinging my pen down on the Court notebook. 'Call an immediate adjournment.'

The air inside was suffocating, so it was a relief to get out onto the verandah, despite the cacophony from the belfry which continued unabated.

'I'm as keen on the rehabilitation of offenders as anyone,' I said to Mr Sharma, as I strode up and down with my hands over my ears, 'but this simply can't go on.'

I paused to accept a glass of water and an aspirin from Constable Josefa.

Trouble with the Padre

'How about your lordship tie your wig under your lordship's chin,' Josefa said, miming the action, 'like Her Majesty Queen Elizabeth's headscarf.' The notion struck me as not only absurd but somehow disrespectful.

I was sitting at my desk in Chambers to think out my next course of action when, unexpectedly, a glorious silence fell. The Canon, it seemed, had called it a day. I instantly returned to the Bench and disposed of the mother-in-law case with a bind-over on both sides, before turning to the rest of the morning list. Little did I foresee that Canon Stubbs was embarking upon nothing less than a daily routine of bell practice! After twelve more days of non-stop Ringing of the Changes my old enemy – Melanesian Migraine – set in. In addition, there was a marked falling-off in staff efficiency under the Canon's relentless bombardment.

The final straw came on a Friday afternoon. I was considering a written submission on behalf of the island's arch-criminal, Sitiveni Thabuka, burglar and mugger-in-chief. Glancing out at the church tower I was startled to see the sinister features of the Ace Recidivist himself! Framed in the belfry window, he bore an eerie resemblance to Charles Laughton as the Hunchback of Notre Dame. With a cheery wave in my direction he swung back on the rope of the largest bell of all – a Lichfield Bass Clapper, according to Canon Stubbs's parish magazine. Even my new earplugs from Ying Chang's Pharmacy proved useless against this onslaught. In desperation I cancelled the order for Prisoners' Leisure Parole. Next day Sitiveni was sent to join the stone-cleaning gang on Easter Island.

Then I had a stroke of true fortune. My official duties included the function of Island Legal Draftsman. The Annual Revision of the Local Ordinances provided me with a chance to defeat the Canon – once and for all. I opened Chapter 2 of the Emergency Byelaws and turned up the heading, Hurricane Warnings. 'Where climatic conditions demand,' it read, 'church bells are to be rung for the notification to the public of this meteorological danger.' Without hesitation I took out my red pencil. AND FOR NO OTHER PURPOSE WHATSOEVER I added, emphasizing the words by way of a thick line. With a light heart I dispatched a note to the Government printer and, forty-eight hours later, under cover of darkness, I pinned a copy of the new enactment upon the Church door.

Even Canon Stubbs hadn't the temerity to challenge the Rule of Law. He carefully avoided all further contact with me and left the colony by the next steamer. Apparently he had given up the living to re-enlist in the Army Chaplaincy. The Canon's successor turned out to be an extremely aged Oxford don. A cleric of mystical inclination, he promptly moved residence to an ashram on the other side of the island.

Shortly afterwards Mr Registrar Sharma had a footnote to add to this information.

'The new Reverend gentleman,' he said with a faint smile, 'has taken the Vow of Eternal Silence.'

Chapter Six

Learning the Drill

IN GENERAL, the position was clear. When it came to penal policy, we judges in the outposts of Empire took our lead from the Mother Country. However, I was well ahead of UK breathalyser legislation when I began my own crackdown on drunken driving. With only one road on the island of Malaika, it was a fairly rare offence, so not surprisingly the case that came before me aroused a great deal of local interest.

The offender was a prosperous-looking tubby gentleman in a striped jacket and sulu. He had been found asleep over the dashboard, his car bonnet through the fence protecting the Little Sisters of St Winifred.

'Winston Roosevelt Lal,' I pronounced, sternly, 'you are hereby fined £400 Pacific Dollars and disqualified until further notice.'

There was a gasp from the crowd of onlookers at the back of the tiny thatched court-house. A dart from a native blow-pipe whistled past my ear.

'Josefa!' I said evenly, 'kindly clear the Public Gallery.'

The defendant's plump face was now contorted with rage.

'The evidence is overwhelming,' I told him. 'It seems that a half-empty drum of palm-toddy was found in the

43

boot of your Morris Oxford, and you yourself proved incapable of getting out of the driving seat.'

Mr Registrar Sharma, normally a stickler for the rigid application of the law, rustled his papers below me. He stood up on his chair and hissed in my ear, 'The defendant is a dentist.'

'What on earth has that got to do with it?' I said.

'The *only* dentist on the island of Malaika,' he persisted. 'Every day he has need of his motor car, making errands of mercy to all the villagers.'

'Mercy!' I snapped. 'There's not much mercy about Mr Lal when he's in his cups. The Mother Superior is still having treatment for nervous shock.'

I studied the defendant's driving licence again.

'And what about this appalling record?'

I pointed to the list of Mr Lal's endorsements – overtaking a bicycle-taxi on the waterfront at high tide, dazzling a herd of goats with a defective headlamp during a cloudburst, and failing to stop after colliding with a bullock-cart – the bullock's right rear leg being still in splints.

'The accused is nothing less than a liability on the roads,' I declared.

'Road,' the Registrar reminded me.

'Well, now at least that vital highway will be safe from the menace of an inebriated Winston Lal,' I said, dismissing the defendant who turned on his heel with a defiant snort.

Unfortunately, all too soon I was to find myself exposed to the menace of Mr Lal in a completely different situation.

I had been celebrating Empire Day with a visit to HM Gaol where the prisoners had entertained me to a meal of boiled rice and curried goat. Regrettably the accompanying dish of grated coconut contained several fragments of coral chippings – some prank on their part no doubt – but the impact of one of them on a back molar proved disastrous. That same night I developed violent toothache.

In the light of morning, my bathroom mirror revealed a jagged gap where a filling had come away. There was nothing else for it. The Registrar made the necessary telephone call and Mr Lal said he would see me at once.

His dental surgery, a tin-roofed building, was to be found close to the harbour on the other side of the island. It was sometimes mistaken by visitors for a Government Rest House, possibly because Mr Lal, a keen patriot, flew the Union Jack night and day from a flagpole above the entrance.

I climbed the wooden steps with all the enthusiasm of a condemned prisoner stepping onto the hangman's trap. Slumped about the ramshackle verandah were a number of 'discharged' patients in various stages of distress. I hurried past them into a room marked Surgery. For those who could not read, there was a sign-writer's impression of a row of gleaming white teeth framed in a crimson smile.

The door swung open onto a giant operating chair that leaned slightly to one side on its pedestal of cracked linoleum. Behind this engine of terror stood Mr Lal in a soiled white coat.

'Small world,' he murmured, his black eyebrows raised.

He pushed back a swivel table on which were arranged a number of unusual-looking instruments and the remains of some sherbert-sweetmeats.

'Please to take a seat on the Bench,' he said with a chuckle.

I complied and pointed to the back of my mouth.

A Case of Bananas

'The pain seems to be coming from a filling that's broken off,' I said. Mr Lal paid no attention. He was preoccupied with some levers at the back of the chair. With a sudden flick of his hairy elbow, he released a catch and I found myself jerked into a prone position.

A few inches above my head a naked bulb swung to and fro as Mrs Lal moved heavily about in the upper room.

'Open wide,' directed Mr Lal. 'Am taking impression.'

I was about to speak but found myself gagged by a large wodge of what felt like cold cement.

'Bite hard,' I was told.

I did my best.

Glancing around, I was not reassured by a highly coloured picture on the wall. This depicted a tribal goddess wearing a garland of human molars. Her single eye, in the centre of her forehead, seemed to be focused on me.

Mr Lal removed the plaster-cast with a sigh.

'Very bad,' he murmured. 'In old age, monkeys have same problem.'

'Sorry?' I said.

He launched into a lecture on the evolution of teeth in the animal kingdom. 'Canines here are necessary for seizing prey, incisors for shredding the flesh,' he explained.

'That hardly applies to my case, Mr Lal,' I demurred. 'Especially as I happen to be a vegetarian.'

'Please do not correct. My credentials are tip-top I can assure you.' He pointed to a gold certificate hanging alongside the goddess. In the bottom left-hand corner was pasted the ambitious features of a youthful Mr Lal.

'Bachelor of Evolutionary Dentistry, Hawaii, 1954', it read.

There was a click of another lever, causing my feet to

rise several inches into the air as Mr Lal's diatribe was resumed.

'The jaw of humans, as with other advanced creatures, has receded,' he continued relentlessly. 'This is giving pressure on pre-molars, thus causing decay. I have to do full dig-out job.'

Leaving me in a kind of bat-like state of suspension he wandered off towards a shelf. There he began to tinker with his instruments, humming to himself. 'Pack up your troubles in your old kit-bag,' he sang under his breath. Out of the corner of my eye I saw him select a large probe, shaped like a corkscrew. Once again he leaned over me in a whirl of garlic fumes.

'Open wide,' he directed.

I hesitated.

'Not to worry, lordship. Hand is steady now. No more toddy. I signed the Pledge last week.'

'I'm glad to hear it,' I said.

He tapped a sensitive nerve meaningfully.

'So my driving ban is no longer necessary I am thinking?'

I declined to comment on this *prima facie* breach of the *sub judice* rule. Wielding his probe, Mr Lal bent closer.

'You understand that I have turned over a new leaf, my lord,' he persisted.

There was a pause.

'Kindly don't refer to current litigation out of court-hours,' I said indistinctly. My protest was cut short as he inserted a clamp and dragged up an antiquated drill.

'Open wide,' he said as the whole building began to vibrate. Behind me I could see Mr Lal's hairy foot working demonically on the treadle behind the chair. Within minutes he had excavated what felt like half the bottom left-hand side of my mouth. He paused to squirt a pink

47

jet of disinfectant into the ruins.

'Rinse,' he commanded.

I flushed out an inordinate amount of assorted debris.

Mr Lal peered into the damage.

Through his magnifying glass the leer upon his face assumed a nightmarish proportion.

'Bloody bad show,' he said. 'Maybe all your lordship's teeth have to be extracted after all.'

He drew my attention to a glass display-cabinet. It was packed with several replicas of the dentures depicted on the sign outside.

'I think I replace teeth everywhere,' he said.

He paused thoughtfully, wrench in hand.

'Or, of course, your lordship might replace licence?'

I tightened my grip on the frayed arms of the chair and levered myself into the upright position.

'Tomorrow,' I said, breathing heavily, 'at 10 a.m. Your application for restoration of driving licence will be considered in my Chambers. On your solemn promise to keep the Pledge, that is.'

'In the meantime, just the single filling,' I went on, with as much authority as I could muster in the circumstances.

Mr Lal nodded with an air of satisfaction.

'OK, Judge. I get dressing ready. Quick job fixed. No more trouble.'

He was as good as his word. Within a quarter of an hour my toothache had vanished.

At five to ten next morning I was at my desk. On the opposite side of the square I saw the dental surgeon approaching the court with a self-important air. Surrounded by well-wishers he mounted the verandah for the last stage in his *cause célèbre*.

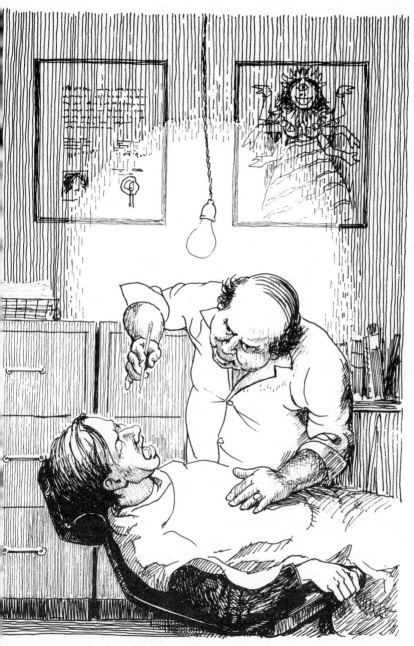

'Open wide,' he directed

A Case of Bananas

'Good morning, lordship,' he said with a deep bow.

'I am glad to read you have indeed mended your ways, Mr Lal,' I replied. I pointed to the morning issue of the *Island Gazette* which Josefa had placed in my in-tray. It carried a blotched photograph of Mr Lal under the headline, 'Island Temperance Association's First Life President'.

'Your licence is provisionally restored,' I told him as I signed the relevant document.

Mr Lal handed me a curious-looking brown-paper parcel.

'A small memento of the occasion,' he explained.

I unwrapped it cautiously.

A plaster-cast of one's teeth is not exactly the ideal desk ornament. With a flash of inspiration, however, I placed it as a paperweight upon my set of Colonial Office legal bulletins.

'And thank you lordship for prompt dispatch of justice,' said Mr Lal, bowing again as he withdrew.

Outside, Mr Lal's son had parked the newly polished Morris Oxford in readiness. I watched from my window as my torturer of the previous day took his place in the driving seat.

Winding down the window, Mr Lal managed to have the last word.

'Old English saying,' he called out to the crowd as he revved away. 'Lordship's bark is worse than his bite!'

Chapter Seven

That Damn Fool Pennington

RIGHT FROM THE START of my colonial career, Commissioner J.S. Pennington had a way of turning up, unexpectedly, rather in the role of an eccentric uncle. J.S. preferred to work as far from officialdom as possible, an arrangement usually favoured by both sides. So I never quite knew where the next encounter would be. There was the day, for instance, when I was summoned by His Excellency the Governor of the remaining Oceanic Territories to Government House.

'It's that damn fool Pennington,' H.E. remarked.

'How do you mean, sir?'

'Seem's he's categorically refused to steer the islanders of Numea towards self-government. Totally ignoring Whitehall policy. And now he's in some kind of trouble, not surprisingly.'

The Governor handed me a cable. It was from Pennington. It was addressed to H.E. REGRET TO INFORM YOU I AM UNDER HOUSE ARREST.

'Bloody idiot,' exploded His Excellency. 'Obviously he's exhausted the patience of the islanders.' He rubbed his balding head with some desperation.

'Since no other judge is available, it seems I have no

choice but to send you out to see what on earth can be done. And while you're there you might as well have a go at a complete rehash of the Constitution.'

The Governor, so it transpired, had already arranged for me to travel on a sloop of the Royal New Zealand Navy.

The Pacific belied its name and the voyage was extremely rough in parts. As the ship heaved her way through the coral shoals I remained in my bunk. Burying myself in Cook's *Travels* I tried to recapture the romance of those eighteenth-century voyagers who had first brought Western civilization to these parts.

Commander Bain was a bluff skipper with a florid complexion and a touch of Captain Bligh about him.

'Up on deck, Knox Mawer,' he bellowed through the speaking tube. 'It's only a bit of a squall!'

Repressing thoughts of mutiny I joined him on the quarter-deck for a barbecue supper, just as the island of Numea appeared on the skyline.

Early next morning we dropped anchor. A bevy of chieftains had gathered on the beach in tarpa loincloths, feathered war-plumes on their heads.

Commander Bain decreed that I should go ashore alone.

'Your job is to bring about some sort of reconciliation,' he pointed out. 'A show of force might well scupper any chance of success.'

He clamped a hand on my shoulder.

'If you need us, we'll be anchored just around the bay.'

A rowing boat took me, along with my faithful orderly, Josefa, as far as the reef. There I rolled up my striped trousers and waded ashore, Josefa following with my wig-box and briefcase.

I rolled up my striped trousers and waded ashore . . .

A Case of Bananas

An imposing Headman advanced from the circle. He was wearing a bright yellow waistcoat with shabby button-holes which I recognized as once having belonged to J.S.

'What have you done with Commissioner Pennington?' I demanded through Josefa, always a reliable interpreter.

The elders showed signs of indignation.

'Our people became very angry,' their Headman explained. 'We were obliged to imprison Big Foot in his bungalow.'

'Big Foot?!' I asked Josefa. 'Are you sure you've got the right translation?'

'It's their own name for Commissioner Pennington,' Josefa replied. 'It's customary to give a totem-name to high Government officials.'

Resolutely I made my way to the village clearing with the chiefs behind me. A row of thatched huts ran along either side. As I passed I could hear the inhabitants muttering to each other in tones of obvious sedition.

'What building was this?' I enquired, pointing to a charred ruin in the centre of the village.

'That was the office of Big Foot,' I was told.

'And the residence of Big Foot?' I enquired sternly.

The Headman pointed to a sprawling wooden bungalow on the top of an adjoining hill where two warriors with sharp eyes and sharper spears stood guard at the gate.

'Come right in,' boomed a familiar voice when I arrived there. 'I'm just dusting the termites off King's College Chapel.'

Inside, the tall, disjointed figure of J.S. Pennington, with his wild thatch of hair, was propped on a stepladder hanging up an old print from his Cambridge days.

'You've come at exactly the right moment.'

That Damn Fool Pennington

He sprang down and donned a pair of thonged san-
dals of biblical shape and size. His totem name, I felt,
was all too appropriate.

'I don't know about "right moment",' I said. 'However, I may be just in time to—'

'In time to lend a hand with this pianola, old chap,'
interrupted J.S. 'Think I've managed an excellent repair
job. Only need a hand to shift it back into that corner.'

'Really J.S.,' I was protesting when a sudden jangling
from the bowels of the instrument totally drowned me
out. J.S. began treading the pedals ferociously.

'No place like home,' he boomed discordantly.
'There's no-o place like home!'

With a low grinding sound the musical accompaniment died away.

'Blast,' J.S. declared, 'the music roll's got stuck
again.'

Impatiently, I turned away and indicated the mountain of documents stacked on his desk.

'At least you've made a start on work on the
Constitution, I see.'

'Dear me no!'

Pennington sprang towards the papers with
enthusiasm.

'These are all my notes on local archaeology,' he said.
'Been investigating the Neolithic diggings on the leew-
ard coast. Riveting stuff.'

He pulled out a large drawer underneath. More files
spilled out.

'And these are my Astrology charts. Movements of
Jupiter and so on. Particularly interesting this time of
year.'

Before I could speak he was halfway up the stepladder
once more.

'You've seen my telescope, of course. It's on the roof.'

A Case of Bananas

'For heaven's sake, J.S.!' I called to him. 'Don't you realize we've an all-out island revolt on our hands?'

It was no use. It had always been impossible to establish a consistent line of thought for more than thirty seconds with J.S. Pennington. He had an incorrigible habit of leaping from one thing to another like a giant grasshopper.

On his last visit to the main township, for instance, he had arranged a frantic non-stop itinerary for himself. This included a course on basket-weaving, coaching lessons for the polo team and a series of lectures for the British Council on Medieval English Churches.

'Perhaps I could borrow that old bike of yours to get around on,' he had said to me at the time. 'The one you've got in your garden shed.'

I came across him, next day, pushing the bicycle at top speed along Marine Parade.

'Why on earth don't you get on it?' I asked, mystified.

'No time! No time! was his reply as he hurried on.

Now here he was again – madly polishing up the lens of an ancient telescope while Rome burnt, so to speak!

He stepped back from the bamboo stand upon which the instrument had been installed.

'Want to have a look?'

'Really, Pennington!' I exclaimed. 'Are we *never* going to discuss what's going on in Numea? Your being held hostage for a start!'

'Don't really mind it,' he beamed. 'Don't mind being housebound at all. Allows one to get things into a bit of order.'

He led the way on to the rear verandah. Pulling on a tattered golfing blazer he flung himself into a cane chair. 'Half-time, dear chap,' he announced. He uncorked an enormous bottle of whisky.

'Care to help me out?'

That Damn Fool Pennington

I shook my head firmly and took out my pocket watch.

'The Governor will be expecting a wireless report care of the Navy within twenty-four hours,' I said. 'So you'd better begin to explain exactly how the trouble started.'

'At the meeting I called to announce self-government,' Pennington replied.

'How long did you say it would take for the official handing-over?' I enquired.

'Didn't get that far,' said Pennington.

He gulped down a second tot. 'Couldn't make myself heard actually.'

I took a deep breath.

'If you didn't even promise them a date for Independence, little wonder they're up in arms!'

My ear caught the ominous rat-tat-tat of a signal-drum from the direction of the village.

'Things are clearly on a knife edge,' I continued.

J.S. chuckled.

'If the worst comes to the worst,' he replied, 'there's another problem.'

'Problem?'

'Question of size you might say.'

'Size?'

'I'm talking about the Regulation Coffin, my boy.'

'Coffin?'

'Surely you know the Public Works Department invariably sends one out to every outpost in cases of emergency.'

I shook my head, lost for words.

'The fools have sent me the wrong size! Standard medium. I ask you! Could be so undignified.'

He turned and inspected me closely.

'Still,' he added, 'should be perfectly alright for you, anyway.'

I moistened my lips with a sip of water. It was more

57

than high time to take a grip on the whole situation.

'The idiocy,' I complained, 'is that a crisis need never have arisen at all. Since Harold Macmillan made his "Wind of Change" speech self-government is a matter of course. The old Colonial Service is already a thing of the past.'

Pennington sighed. He was off on a tangent again. 'Ah, the old colonial days, the old colonial characters! Did I ever tell you about Tuffy Harbottle in North Borneo?' he went on animatedly. 'Dinner party at GH. Tuffy arrived late. Totally plastered. When we stood up to drink the Royal Toast Tuffy drained the nearest flower vase and collapsed into the stilton. Idea was to be certified troppo and sent home passage-paid. Didn't work though. Got promoted to Governor in the West Indies instead.'

I was listening with only half an ear. My attention was concentrated on the sight of tribesmen gathering under the flame trees. Their powerful bodies glistened with war-paint.

'I'll have to get a message to Commander Bain at once,' I told J.S.

'Did you mention Commander Bain?' he said. 'His ship called in last year. We had rather a binge. Woke up in the morning with my wallet in the fridge and the last can of beer in the safe.'

'To hell with your binge,' I snapped. 'Something far more unpleasant is going to happen if I don't act straight away.'

Suddenly, the situation became crystal clear in my mind.

'I must deliver a public address at once,' I said. 'Put things straight before it's too late.'

Pennington obediently pulled out a whistle from his pocket and blew it three times. One of the guards came sprinting over from the gate.

That Damn Fool Pennington

'Tell the people to assemble in the village square,' Pennington directed. With a salute, the messenger departed at a trot.

'Of course, it'll have to be in the open air,' J.S. told me. 'Expect you noticed my old HQ has gone up in smoke. Not that it was any loss. Front used to fall down every time I fired the cannon.'

'The cannon?'

'Special salute for Royal Birthdays,' he explained.

J.S. lay back and closed his eyes.

'Afraid you'll have to go it alone at the meeting,' he murmured. 'As you know, I'm not allowed to step outside this place. Good luck anyway.'

Below the front steps one of the guards was waiting to escort me to the village.

Once there, I found a bellicose throng already gathered. I stepped up on to a large log.

'Men of Numea,' I began.

Josefa translated my address.

'I have been sent by the Governor with full permission to accede to popular demand.'

Encouraging smiles greeted this announcement.

'No doubt,' I continued, 'when Mr Pennington first addressed you on the subject you were fearing "procrastination" on his part.'

Josefa had a struggle at this point but seemed to manage some sort of translation.

'It is my special privilege, however,' I went on, 'to promise you self-government as soon as it can be arranged. Say the year after next.'

The crowd gave vent to a furious roar.

I checked myself and tried again.

'Very well. Let us say next year.'

Screams of rage. Brandishing of clubs.

59

A Case of Bananas

'Immediate self-government then,' I cried. 'You can have independence tomorrow.'

Within seconds I was surrounded by the mob. My only chance was to play for time.

'I insist that the Commissioner be sent for immediately,' I said.

The elders put their heads together.

'Big Foot must be here,' I repeated.

To my surprise, my demand was accepted.

The next minute, in an excited hubbub, Pennington was brought down to join me, rubbing the sleep from his eyes.

'What on earth have you been telling them?' he wanted to know.

'I've announced Independence,' I said. 'What more could I do?'

'But that's just the point,' exploded Pennington. 'They don't want Independence!'

'Don't want it?'

'That's what I've been trying to tell you. Only you never give me a chance to get a word in edgeways.'

I groaned.

'So what do we do?' I said.

'Reassure them. Tell them that you didn't mean it.'

With a final effort, I gathered myself together.

Painted faces drew nearer and I could feel heavy breathing down the back of my neck.

'Well, gentlemen,' I began, speaking like a man in a trance, 'if you don't want to govern yourselves you don't have to.'

This statement roused grunts of approval.

'Although,' I said, 'it is the policy of HMG to grant independence to all colonial territories.'

Savage mutterings stirred again.

I raised my hand. 'But no doubt an exception can be

made of the island of Numea.'

Tumultuous applause broke out on every side.

'High time for tiffin,' said J.S., with a satisfied air, striding away back to his house.

Before following him, I beckoned to Josefa.

'There is one thing I need to know.'

The elders clustered forward.

'Would you like the Governor to arrange a change of Commissioner? New blood, so to speak?'

The suggestion aroused immediate opposition. Bird of Paradise plumes were tossed violently to and fro. Spear in hand the Headman stepped forward, to explain in the best English he could muster.

'Why do you think we shut Big Foot into his house in the first place?' he demanded. I looked puzzled.

'Because we need to keep him with us. Always!' he added sternly.

'I take your point,' I said.

Back on the beach, Pennington and I shook hands.

'The Governor's going to look pretty foolish,' I said, 'with no change of policy after all this fuss and expense.'

I moved off towards the naval boat waiting for me by the reef.

'There's just one thing the Governor could change though,' Pennington called out.

'What's that?' I asked.

'Tell him to send me a decent-size coffin, for Pete's sake.'

J.S.'s last words floated out on the breeze.

'But not for another year or so. Got too much work to do.'

Chapter Eight

A Case of Bananas

ON 31 MARCH 1884 a strangely wrapped and much-travelled package arrived at Windsor Castle. It was addressed to Queen Victoria and was opened with caution over a bucket of water. The Queen's life had been threatened in anarchist quarters so it was best to be on the safe side. The inner wrappings consisted of palm leaves. However, it was the content itself which aroused the greatest astonishment.

Dexterously set in coral was a complete set of human teeth arranged in an enormous smile. The accompanying message read:

> To Her Majesty Queen Victoria, Queen of Great Britain, First Empress of all the Empires of the world. We the King and Nobles of Tavula desire to pray your Majesty to accept this token of our esteem and earnest good wishes for your future happiness. With it we send our humble plea that Your Majesty will stretch out towards us your mighty hand that Tavula may hide in it and be safe.

The letter was signed by the Reverend Ezekiel Williams, Methodist Missionary, on behalf of King Kaivunda I.

At the time, sad to say, the request was completely

A *Case of Bananas*

ignored. A letter of thanks was dispatched by Sir Henry Ponsonby, Queen Victoria's Private Secretary, for what Sir Henry described as 'this most unusual gift', but no reference was made to the petition that Tavula should become part of the British Empire.

Not until the German Kaiser acquired the neighbouring island of Sampa was Tavula deemed worthy of Britannic protection. It was an example of the haphazard way in which we collected our possessions around the world. Three years later, HMS *Rapid* was dispatched to the island and the Union Jack planted on the beach to the applause of the local population.

The Pax Britannica brought one immediate boon to the people of Tavula. New laws promptly put an end to slave trading, or 'blackbirding', as it was known in the South Seas. In those days, with no visiting judge on hand, the culprits were brought to book by the Royal Navy. The naval captain, who held the necessary court, cut through legal technicalities in a typically breezy manner – if the sea-stained old register in the Suba museum is anything to go by.

In 1899, for instance, a particularly notorious blackbirder, one William Perkins, came before Commander Montgomery-Fitzhugh RN. He met with little sympathy for the injury he had received upon resisting capture.

> *Fitzhugh* Hold up your right hand, Perkins, your testimony has to be on oath.
>
> *Perkins* Sorry, your honour, my right arm be broke with grapeshot.
>
> *Fitzhugh* Hold up your left, then, you villain.
>
> *Perkins* Cannot oblige there neither, your honour. Bosun's cutlass got me fair and square on the shoulder.
>
> *Fitzhugh* Well, hold up your leg, man. You've got to hold up something in a Court of Law!

A Case of Bananas

Perkins swiftly complied. The alternative might have seen him thrown to the sharks for perjury! The register merely notes that he was duly transported for trial at the Old Bailey and ended his days in Dartmoor prison.

Sixty years later, the honour of trying blackbirders had descended to me, although by that time such scoundrels had ceased to exist. In fact, as far as Tavula was concerned, serious crime was practically extinct. The usual petty misdemeanours – minor affray, domestic assault and so on – were dealt with by the village elders. My services were only sought upon a single occasion, to clear up some long-standing inheritance disputes over land.

The request came from King Kaivunda IV, the present ruler. He was the last reigning monarch in the Melanesian Pacific – apart from his aunt, Queen Fahiti of Tamoa – a formidable lady who once confiscated a pair of my court trousers. But that is another story.

With my invitation to Tavula came a ticket to travel there by plane. ROYAL TAVULAN AIRLINES INC was the heading on the gold-lettered card, below the Royal Crest – a crown surmounting two crossed bananas rampant.

The aircraft itself was a four-seater, piloted by a former member of the Luftwaffe, Oberleutnant Augustus Von Stopfel. Von Stopfel had retired to manage a pilchard factory in Samoa, but liked to practise aviation as a hobby. An elderly man, with an iron jaw and cropped grey head, he turned to greet me as I climbed aboard with Josefa, my Orderly. 'You vos in zee var?' he demanded.

'Not in the airforce,' I added hastily.

'No matter,' he replied, glaring at me through mad blue eyes. 'I vill show you.'

The aviator pulled on an old pair of goggles and hunched himself over the controls. The next minute we roared across the field into take-off, banking in a side-ways flip over the reef. Below us a party of fishermen ducked to cover in their canoe.

'Zis little plane is reminding me of zee dog-fights,' he shouted back over the roar of the engine.

Suddenly, we lurched upwards into a half-loop. Von Stopfel threw back his head and laughed loudly.

'Now I am catching up vith zee Spitfire, eh! Vatch out.'

I kept my eyes closed for the rest of the trip. Best to pretend, I decided, that I was back at the fairground in Rhyl where my schoolfriend, Donald Rathbone, had once persuaded me to join him on the rollercoaster Demon Dipper.

I must have blacked out behind Oberleutnant Von Stopfel because the next thing I knew we were bumping to a halt between a row of coconut trees.

'I return you on next week's flight, ya?'

'Very kind,' I said, 'but I'm already booked on a steamer, I'm afraid.'

A solemn Tavulan official in a peaked-cap of wartime vintage was awaiting me in the Customs Shed. After inspecting my documents, he brought down a rubber-stamp on the back of my hand. The Tavulan Crest, in bright green ink, proved extremely difficult to remove, and was later the cause of another misunderstanding with my Chief Justice.

'Really, Knox Mawer!' Sir Neville complained. 'If you're going in for tattoos at least you might keep them out of sight!'

Josefa loaded me and my belongings aboard a small wooden bus with the inscription, Tit-for-Tat Motor Services, painted along the offside. In a cloud of dust we set off along a narrow track leading to the township. Its main street was lined with the usual weatherboard stores, and a stray pig hurried out of our way in the nick of time. Dusk was falling and the place seemed deserted.

'Everyone is getting ready for the Banana Festival,' the driver explained.

'Festival?' I shook my head. Wherever I went on circuit it seemed there was always a local ceremony in progress of one kind or another.

'I trust it doesn't interfere with the court I've come to hold,' I observed tersely.

'Festival first,' beamed the driver. 'Court later.'

A vine-covered bungalow came into view, bearing the sign, Home for Foreign Visitors. Beneath it stood a white-haired island lady in a flowered pinafore.

'I am Aunty Hibiscus. Tea is ready.'

She led me to a lace-covered table on the verandah. Upon it stood a steaming urn containing an enormous ham and several boiled eggs. There was also an iced cake with the words, 'Welcome Judge', picked out in cherries.

She pulled out a stool and patted me on the shoulder.

'I know about English taste,' she said. 'My late husband was a merchant navy cook, sailing from Southampton.'

Josefa accepted a slice of cake but then had to hurry off to the local cinema. *Dracula's Castle of Blood* was showing, one of his favourites, and there was bound to be a full house.

Next morning I was awoken by distant chanting and the rattle of biscuit-tin drums. Looking out, I could see what appeared to be a gigantic mass of greenery on the move. It was surging down the street, singing loudly.

'They are the dancers,' explained Aunty Hibiscus, as she served me bacon and eggs.

The forest transformed itself into a procession of villagers in leafy skirts and garlands. Tall ferns nodded

A Case of Bananas

from a hundred heads, while strings of shells around their ankles clashed together in time to a male-voice choir.

They were making for the Royal Palace, a stately white stucco building, rather like a three-star Victorian hotel, which was just visible beyond the flame trees.

'What's it all about?' I asked Josefa.

'Every year it is the custom for the islanders to present the first fruits of the season to the King,' he replied. 'You are to have a place of honour with His Majesty at the Royal Stand.'

Josefa's instructions from the Palace were to escort me, fully arrayed in wig and gown, to the ceremonial arena in the Palace grounds. There we discovered King Kaivunda IV already seated on the dais. A rotund, buddha-like figure, HM was flanked by nobles in tarpa-cloth robes. Nervously, I bowed to the King before taking my allotted place nearby. The beach in front of us provided a natural platform. It was decorated here and there with large branches of bananas laid upon altars of driftwood.

At a signal from the Monarch, the court flautist hurried forward to give a solo performance upon the Tavulan nose flute. This unique instrument is of considerable interest to collectors of curios. However, its design renders it incapable of producing more than three melancholy notes.

After forty-five minutes of the ancient Banana Serenade I found myself beginning to nod off. Luckily, at this point, the flute player was replaced by a merry throng of string musicians armed with a quaint collection of ukuleles and guitars.

'This is a famous band,' Josefa informed me in a whisper. 'Very clever fellows. They make their own instruments in the prison workshop.'

The opening number had something of the tempo of an eightèenth-century gavotte. After the introductory bars, the King got slowly to his feet. There was a rustle of excitement amongst the crowd of spectators as His Majesty turned towards me.

'Shall we dance?' he said.

Taken aback, I rose with a curtsy, straightened my gown and shook back the curls in my wig. It seemed there was nothing else for it. I cannot say how many judges have tried to *chassé* in buckle shoes – especially on the powdery sand of a South Sea lagoon. In my case it was not made any easier by being locked in the embrace of a 24-stone partner.

'We call this the Mekotuvani,' His Majesty explained. 'Only my own personal household is permitted to take part.'

The attendant members of the aristocracy fell back respectfully as we circled a giant pyramid, in the centre of the enclosure, consisting – so I was told – of 1000 bunches of Gros Michel bananas.

I think I would have managed alright had the drummer, seated at the lali, not quickened the tempo so dramatically. Nimble footed, for all his weight, the king whirled me round like a top. Somehow or other I went spinning out of control and came to an abrupt halt right in the middle of the massed banjoes of the prison band. Wild applause greeted this untimely exhibition on my part. I drew myself up with what dignity I could muster. 'Permission to adjourn, Your Majesty,' I said stiffly . . .

Resting in my room that afternoon, I was going through the case-papers for the next day when there was a screech of brakes outside. Peering out over the verandah, I saw a burly red-faced European in a soiled bush-jacket jump out of a decrepit lorry.

'Digger Burke's the name, squire,' he called up to me. 'And I've come for Justice.'

It was my policy to make myself available at all times to members of the public, however unprepossessing they might seem.

'You'd better come in, Mr Burke,' I said.

Flinging down his greasy bush-hat, my visitor advanced up the steps menacingly. He threw a bundle of documents on to Aunty Hibiscus's swing seat, then took out a hip flask.

'Drink first, Judge?' he said, unscrewing the top.

Shaking my head, I retreated from the fumes of home-brewed rum toddy.

'Please yourself,' he said.

He took an enormous swig.

'Now then, sport,' he began, 'what I need to know is whether the law is on my side or the King's.'

In long and rambling sentences he explained that he owned the largest banana plantation on Tavula.

'See that lot,' he said, pointing to the mountain of bananas glistening in the distant sunset over the Royal enclosure. 'The best of my Gros Michels. The jokers come and took their pick while me back was turned, without as much as a by your leave.

'All ready they were for shipping to New Zealand tomorrer.'

He bared his teeth.

'And all for some heathen bloody knees-up for the King. It's downright robbery.'

'You chose to settle here, Mr Burke,' I said calmly, moving behind a pot of ferns. 'The King is regarded as a divine being. You know better than I that the first fruits are a sacred offering. To ensure the island's prosperity.'

Unfortunately, my answer seemed only to enrage him

I cannot say how many judges have tried to chassé in buckle shoes

A Case of Bananas

further. He had got up and was now towering over me.

'As well as pinching all me best bananas his blinking Majesty levied a 150 per cent tax on 'em.'

To my alarm, he seemed to be trying to unbuckle his belt. 'So what are you going to do about it?'

'Do sit down, Mr Burke,' I urged. 'The law concerning bananas on Tavula is clear. The King is entitled to tax all produce grown on island soil.'

For a blissful moment my caller turned his attention back to the hip flask.

'Might have known I'd get nowhere with a pommie judge,' he declared, surveying me with a bleary eye. 'Any more than me ancestor did when they shipped him in irons to Botany Bay. All he'd done was run the landlord through in a brawl on his fiftieth birthday.'

My patience was wearing thin.

'I refuse to discuss the matter further, Mr Burke,' I told him. 'I shall be dealing with certain other legal matters in His Majesty's Privy Council tomorrow. If you wish to report to the Palace at that time, such merit as there may be in your complaint can be openly raised in the presence of the King himself. Good afternoon.'

Mr Burke spat a large stream of tobacco-juice over the verandah rail. 'Well, you'd better be sharp about it,' he said. 'Unless I get those Michels on the steamer for Auckland on time I'll be tipping the flaming lot into the Royal swimming bath.'

After a few more muttered oaths the excited Queenslander finally returned to his vehicle and drove off into the night.

With Mr Burke's intemperate petition on my mind, sleep was out of the question. I have always found that, when the responsibilities of office press hard upon me, the only answer is to burn the midnight oil upon quiet research.

71

A Case of Bananas

It was my practice never to venture on circuit without Flyte's *Exchequer Causes* (the annotated edition by Cozens-Hardy, Master of the Rolls), Volumes 1 and 2. Even so, it was not until the early hours that I discovered, in Volume 2, the vital precedent for which I had been searching.

'Upon an Issue pertaining to ye Royal Prerogative,' the passage read (the flattened corpse of a spike termite had defaced the bottom of that particular page, but it was still readable), 'upon such Issue – the wise judge doth conciliate privily between ye parties.'

I woke next morning with these words in mind. I was due to present myself at the Privy Council Chamber at 10 a.m. The crowds had dispersed but the banana mountain was still in place. The royal gardeners were reverently hosing it down as I made my way across to the Council Chamber. This was a chapel-like building of Pacific Gothic design, annexed to the Palace. The national flag of crossed bananas flew from the spire. To my surprise, I was greeted at the stained oak door by the Clerk of Council, a dignified noble in a starched white tunic.

'His Majesty,' he explained, 'would like you to join him at the Turtle Pool.'

The pool was alongside the lagoon, a rush-fenced enclosure under the acacia trees. The Monarch himself was standing in the shallows, a striking figure swathed in an immense scarlet towel. Fresh from his morning dip he seemed in a mellow mood.

'Good morning, Judge. I trust you've recovered.'

He handed me a large basketful of breadfruit.

'Thank you, Your Majesty,' I said, 'but I've already breakfasted.'

'No, no,' he laughed, 'it's feeding time for my pets.'

A Case of Bananas

To demonstrate, he threw a handful of husks to the scaly heads bobbing about above the surface of the water. 'The turtles have a happy life, until they end up as soup,' he said.

'The court-sitting, Your Majesty,' I ventured after a few minutes. 'A Privy Council Judicial Committee will be convened as arranged?'

'Actually, no,' said the King.

He was now reclining on a nearby rock and gestured for me to join him. An attendant appeared and began to anoint him with scented coconut oil.

'All the cases have ended without your assistance, Judge,' declared the King mysteriously.

'Really, Your Majesty?'

'Yes, indeed. Nature has her own way of doing these things in Tavula.'

'I don't quite understand, sir.'

'They were property feuds, as you know, going back many years. It happens that the last disputant passed away three weeks ago. Now all the deceased may put their claims before the Supreme Judge, Jehovah.'

He chuckled.

'If the missionaries are to be believed, that is!'

There was a surreptitious movement on the far side of a neatly trimmed frangipani hedge at the edge of the Palace grounds. The lurking figure of Digger Burke could be seen, with a parked lorry beside him.

'Well, Your Majesty,' I explained, 'an additional matter has arisen, rather an urgent one, I'm afraid.'

Donning a pair of outsized sunglasses with ornate white rims, His Majesty listened attentively.

'It should be dealt with immediately,' I continued. 'Now that we happen to have time.'

'What is this time you English keep talking about?' the King teased. 'It's nothing but an old clock you have to keep winding up. Life doesn't need winding up, does it, Judge?'

'True, Your Majesty,' I said. 'But Mr Burke over there is exceedingly wound up. If you will pardon the joke!'

I pointed in the direction of the lorry.

'Ah, Mr Burke!' His Majesty frowned. 'Yes. That, indeed, will mean something urgent.'

He pulled on a massive floral bathing wrap.

'Perhaps we'd better go inside,' I was told.

The King's Den, as he called it, was a corner of the upstairs Palace balcony, with bamboo blinds drawn down against the heat. Seated at the opposite end of an embroidered mat, I laid out the argument on behalf of Mr Burke. After a few moments' reflection the King called for a bowl of kava, and together we worked out a reasonable compromise. This would allow Digger Burke a rebate of banana tax with permission to remove his bananas for shipment forthwith. On my way out, I reported the proposed terms to Mr Burke. He was more than satisfied. 'Good on yer, swagman,' he said.

He brought out two cans of Fosters lager. Ignoring my protest, he forced them, one into each side-pocket of my black alpaca jacket.

'Now I'll be getting on with me loading,' were his finalwords.

My own ship was not due to leave until the following day. That evening the programme of musical entertainment was resumed at the Palace. I tried to excuse myself but the King was insistent. Upon this occasion the prison band became particularly animated, and it was with a sinking heart that I recognized the all too-familiar strain of the Mekotuvani. In vain I tried to avoid the royal eye. The next minute an enormous hand was clamped around my neck.

'Shall we dance?' said the King.

Chapter Nine

A Spot of Home Leave

I SOMETIMES ASK MYSELF whether I was born under a particularly unlucky star. Surely, for other people, collecting shells on the beach is a pretty harmless occupation. So why, in my case, should it land me in a hospital bed?

I don't want to go through the whole embarrassing episode. Suffice it to say that, before leaving Tavula, I had been roped into the King's latest brainchild – The Royal Melanesian Surfing Club. Despite his immense girth His Majesty had proved himself a first-class surfer, zooming across the breakers of Tavula Bay like a human hovercraft, to the respectful applause of his courtiers gathered on the shore.

In his enthusiasm the Monarch insisted that I take up the sport under his personal tuition. But one crash-landing, entangled with the Royal surfing board, was enough for me.

'Perhaps you do not have sufficient weight,' His Majesty observed, munching a water-melon at the picnic by the lagoon afterwards.

'Still, practice makes perfect, Judge.'

It was to avoid another lesson that I made my excuses to the royal party and set off to hunt for shells in the next bay. Ironically enough, after avoiding serious injury in the surf, I found myself laid low by a mere slip on a coral reef. My unexpected sighting of the rare blue-spotted cowrie was the cause of my accident. However, a surface graze was all that it seemed at first and, after Josefa had bandaged me up, I thought all was well.

This was fortunate as it was time for me to take a well-earned spot of home leave in the United Kingdom. J.S. Pennington had kindly booked me into Windycot, his sister's private guesthouse on Exmoor and I attributed the odd twinge I was getting in my foot to the icy temperature of Miss Pennington's establishment. But when I moved on to a London hotel for a change of scene it was still giving me trouble.

Then came the evening when I was treating Aunt Sylvia to a performance of *Salad Days* at the Vaudeville. She had noticed that I was limping. 'Nothing at all,' I said, 'one has to expect this sort of thing in the remoter atolls of the South Pacific.'

Halfway through the show, however, I was seized with violent cramp. Thanks to Aunt Sylvia I was promptly delivered by taxi to the Hospital of Tropical Medicine at Paddington.

Next morning my worst fears were confirmed by the frowning face of the Senior Consultant at the side of my bed.

'Coral poisoning, laddie,' said Dr Gordon. 'Did nobody warn you?'

'No,' I replied feebly.

'If we don't pump you full of special antibodies for the next seven days you'll be hopping round like Long John Silver for the rest of your days!'

He glanced at his papers.

'Besides, you look in poorish shape generally. I'm keeping you in the Isolation Ward for another fortnight, while we run through some tests.'

A Spot of Home Leave

Eventually, after two and a half weeks, the doctor came in with his final report.

'You're good for another tour after all,' he said.

'I was planning a short package holiday across the Channel,' I told him, 'a tour of the tulip fields in Holland with my aunt, as a matter of fact.'

He nodded.

'Aye. You'll be fit for the Harwich boat train in a day or two.'

He handed back the dark glasses I was obliged to wear.

'You'll have to keep these on for a few days,' he explained. 'All these injections will make you sensitive to glare for a while.'

He glanced critically at my straggling locks and fourteen-day stubble.

'At least you'll be able to get along to the Hospital barber now you're out of Isolation. But not until tomorrow. I need to take your blood pressure later today.'

'Can I just pop out for an hour? I need to call at Petty France for my passport visas.'

'Right. But take it easy. That final course of sulphonomides was a very strong one.'

Within minutes, I had slipped into a pair of slacks and cardigan. 'Back shortly,' I assured the Ward Sister. I hurried down the stairs, planning to pick up the first bus.

'Haven't you a coat, sir?' inquired Mr Chivers, the hospital porter.

'Summer's not quite over yet, is it?' I enquired.

'Better take this – it's pouring outside.'

He handed me an exceedingly large black raincoat which had seen better days.

'We keep a few for long-term patients. Government issue 1940. The firewatchers used to wear them.'

A Case of Bananas

I thanked him, then remembered something vital.

'Could you lend me a fiver, Mr Chivers? Everything's with Sister, even my wallet, and she's off till five.'

Mr Chivers obliged.

'Won't be more than a jiffy,' I told him.

He took my arm as I swayed on the top step.

'Go slow, sir. Those drugs take time to wear off, you know.'

I certainly did feel rather strange as I stumbled aboard a red London bus, almost missing my foothold.

'No change, old timer,' declared the conductor when I produced the fiver.

'It's all I've got,' I explained.

An old lady next to me pressed a coin into my hand.

'God bless you, poor man,' she said.

'I think he's the one who plays the violin at Oxford Circus Underground,' she whispered to the conductor.

I was still puzzling this out when the bus stopped at Victoria. It was stuffy inside and I decided to get out. It would do me good to walk up Victoria Street, turn left past St James's Station, and go through the park. I glanced at the station clock. There was just time for a cup of tea and a bite to eat.

Attaching myself to a long queue, I picked up a tray. Jostled past the various counters, I must have been helping myself at random. I was still in a bit of a spin. The dark glasses certainly didn't help.

'One tea, one Coca-Cola, one chocolate swirl, four milk-shakes, two jumbo jellies, apricot jam, and a tomato ketchup.'

The cashier shook her head as she rattled off my selection on the cash machine. I was thirsty and had already drunk a milk-shake while still in the queue.

'Money please!'

'Sorry?'

A Spot of Home Leave

'We're not the Salvation Army, you know!'

I began rummaging through the mac pockets for the fiver. In vain! It must have slipped through one of the many holes in the lining.

'Are you going to pay for that milk-shake or not?' she said, removing the remaining items from my tray.

She seemed indifferent to my explanation. A babble of comment from the customers behind greeted the arrival of the Security Officer.

'I do think this is an awful fuss over such a small item,' I protested. 'I'm just on my way to Petty France and if . . .'

'You're nowhere near Petty France, mate,' interrupted the Security Officer. 'Let's be having a few words with you in the office.'

It was a stupid and exasperating situation although, in the circumstances, I'd no alternative save to comply. Unfortunately, when I did get into the Security department, one of my dizzy spells came on.

'I've been in hospital, you understand, and—' I started again.

'Just sip this glass of water, while we see what you've got on you by way of identification.'

I'd already told him that I could not pay for a phone call.

'If you'd only reverse the charges,' I repeated.

The Security Officer ran his hands over my clothing.

'He's got no wallet or papers of any kind,' he said, turning to a colleague. 'I don't like that slur in his speech, either.'

He turned to me again.

'Any coke on you?'

'My Coca-Cola was confiscated with the rest of my refreshments,' I replied with an attempt at dignity.

The Security Officer and his colleage conferred

together in whispers at the other side of the office.

'We'll be back when we've checked the information you've given us,' he said. 'Got to the bottom of your actual identity!'

He looked me up and down with some exasperation.

'I don't suppose the Night Shelter gave you much of a breakfast.'

His companion slid the tea-pot in my direction.

'Get a cuppa down while you've got the chance. From the look of you, you need it.'

The gentleman on the bench next to me had something stronger to hand. 'Have a swig,' he said, proffering half a bottle of rum. 'Calms the nerves something wonderful.'

I shook my head.

'The name's Charlie,' he said, lifting the bottle to his lips.

'Mine's Knox Mawer.'

I put my head between my knees.

Charlie scratched his cheek thoughtfully.

'This bloody business of establishing identity,' he went on, 'can last for hours!'

I sighed. Instantly a legal precedent formed in my mind.

'It took the Tichbournes five years,' I said.

The Security Officer looked in at the door.

We've checked the name you've given us with the passport office in Petty France,' he said. 'They're sending one of their clerks here to make some sort of inquiry.'

He left the room again.

'Who was this geezer Tichbourne, gov?' asked Charlie, who obviously had time on his hands for a chat.

'Well,' I began, 'if you're really interested, the Tichbourne case was one of the most famous in English legal history. Identity was the essential issue.'

'Are you in the law then?' asked Charlie.

'I'm a colonial judge on leave, as a matter of fact,' I said, 'but I can't get these blighters to believe me.'

The eyes of my companion rounded in interest.

'It's a bleeding disgrace, your honour,' he exploded.

I felt a wave of reassurance at the familiar form of address. At least someone trusted my word. It was an emotional moment.

'Borrow this,' said Charlie. He produced a grimy handkerchief.

I replaced my glasses and pulled myself together.

'Go on then,' Charlie encouraged.

'Well, there was the equally notorious mistaken identity case of Adolf Beck,' I continued. 'Ten women swore that he was guilty of obtaining by fraud. Lost his liberty for seven years. And all the time it was a criminal called John Smith.'

I clicked my tongue. 'A major blight on our judicial system if ever there was one.'

The door opened and I was beckoned into an adjoining cubicle. This time, a forbidding female clerk confronted me across a large desk. 'I'm Miss Larimer. From the Petty France passport office,' she informed me. 'What you claim to have sent us is only a temporary passport. We can only begin to check you out on our files if you explain what happened to the permanent one.'

I sat down wearily in a chair. One of my headaches had started.

'What were the circumstances in which your previous passport came to be lost?'

'It was eaten by sharks, believe it or not,' I replied.

Miss Larimer stiffened.

'It happened in the Savage Isles,' I went on.

I wiped my brow with Charlie's handkerchief.

A Case of Bananas

She glanced towards the Security Officer who was guarding the door.

'Could be a maniac. Obviously, some disturbance of the mental process.'

'It was the Queen's fault,' I continued.

Miss Larimer put down her pen carefully.

'The Queen?'

'I'm referring to Her Majesty Queen Fahiti of Tamoa,' I plunged on.

Miss Larimer flared her nostrils and started to drum her bony fingers on the desk.

'I was holding the criminal sessions on one of her islands, you see,' I proceeded. 'Tamoa, it was. I was wearing my best court trousers for the occasion. The Queen took a fancy to them. Never seen striped bags before.'

Miss Larimer turned to the Security Officer. 'We're not going to get anywhere with this one,' she said.

'Do try to understand,' I insisted. 'I'm talking about the South Seas where, as I keep telling you, I am a circuit judge of some experience. It may seem odd. I administer British law but I also have to respect local custom. When a tribal ruler expresses a certain wish, diplomacy requires that it be complied with. There was nothing for it but a quick change on my part. In next to no time my trousers were flying from the mast of the Royal Barge as a symbol of *mana*!'

I paused.

'*Mana* is the Melanesian word for power,' I added, by way of explanation.

Miss Larimer leaned back and covered her face with her hands.

'After a very busy day,' she snapped, 'I am getting extremely tired.'

'So am I, madam,' I countered, 'but please hear me out.'

82

A Spot of Home Leave

'All this happened during the hurricane season,' I gabbled on. 'There was a sudden gust of wind – typical hurricane weather – it detached my trousers from the mast and sent them flying into the breakers.'

I paused for breath. The Security Officer rolled his eyes heavenwards.

'And that was the very last I saw of a vital part of my clothing, together with my passport. It was buttoned up in the back pocket, you see.'

Miss Larimer had clearly reached the end of her patience.

'Maybe this does sound a bit on the far-fetched side,' I agreed. 'On the other hand, surely somebody must have got through to the hospital by now and had my credentials established once and for all. It's quite simple—'

I tried to go on, but the room seemed to be getting into a bit of a spin.

'The telephone line has been engaged for the last half-hour,' barked Miss Larimer.

Her voice sounded distant.

The roaring in my ears increased . . .

Then came oblivion.

When I came to, I found myself looking up into the familiar face of Dr Gordon.

'A case of premature discharge,' he rasped. 'I did warn you, for heaven's sake.'

He put away his stethoscope.

'Now it's definitely forty-eight hours before I let you loose in the outside world again.'

'Make it as long as you like, doctor,' I said gratefully.

The Consultant turned to the Sister.

'Is there anything else you think he needs?'

'Yes, Dr Gordon,' she replied firmly. 'An *urgent* appointment with the barber.'

Chapter Ten

A Law for All Seasons

'DOWN THIS, OLD BOY,' chortled Austin Bolsover QC. 'Put a bit of colour into those pallid cheeks of yours. It's our finest port, normally kept by us Benchers for our own consumption.'

Bolsover had risen to considerable eminence since the days when we were penniless fellow-pupils in Lincolns Inn. Thirty years later we had met, by chance, at the entrance to the library cloakroom – Bolsover, in a hurry as usual, had accidentally trapped me in the swing door. My reward was an invitation, as his guest, to the annual Judges' Dinner given by the ruling elite in Middle Temple Hall.

'Where exactly are you jungle-judging just now?' he enquired, his florid features wreathed in the smoke of a large cigar.

'Salu-salu,' I replied.

'Ah, the Cannibal Isles – if my school atlas was anything to go by.'

He poked a finger into my ribs.

'No wonder you managed to escape the cooking-pot, dear chap. Not much of a feast for the fuzzy-wuzzies here!'

Bolsover rocked to and fro, laughing helplessly, only pulling himself together as the gong was struck at the top table.

84

A Law for All Seasons

'Be upstanding, gentlemen,' boomed the principal speaker, Baron Parkhurst. 'I ask you to drink a toast to the great institution of British Justice. As someone has so rightly described it, a Law for All Seasons!'

I sighed. To the noble speaker, I thought a shade resentfully, it was no more than a catch-phrase. But for someone like myself, striving to adapt the English legal system to all manner of alien climates and cultures, it was a motto of grim reality.

A Law for All Seasons! I took another sip of port. What, I asked myself, did Baron Parkhurst know of the hazards of holding court at the onset of the rains on Moldini Island, for instance? In my mind's eye I could visualize, all too clearly, the savage flash of sheet lightning and the confusion that followed as the primitive electric generator fell victim to the storm. The flickering flame of a tilly-lamp was hardly the ideal form of illumination by which to consult the small print of Archbold's *Criminal Practice Evidence and Procedure*. To add to my difficulty on that particular occasion, I was trying one of the gravest offences in the Moldini Penal Code – a felonious conspiracy to cast a spell of impotence on the newly married Chief. Incessant peals of thunder interrupted my summing-up. As the rain beat like tom-toms on the tin roof overhead, I struggled to drive home a direction to the jury on the corroboration of an accomplice's evidence. By the time I had finished the row of twelve bemused villagers, ensconced as was their custom in rattan-hammocks, had fallen asleep.

'Wakey! Wakey!' said Austin Bolsover in my ear, jerking me out of my own reverie. Baron Parkhurst was still on his feet, now holding forth on the solemn and sacred customs of British judicial office. 'Hallowed tradition,' he was declaiming, 'requires by way of illustration that we retain our age-old court dress, whatever may be the fickle changing fashions of the twentieth century.'

Quite so, I thought to myself, although in temperatures of 115° Fahrenheit the scarlet and ermine posed problems, the nature of which none of my fellow diners would appreciate. The solution, I found, was to strip off completely underneath save for a pair of airtex briefs and a string vest.

Unfortunately, on my way to court in Nasairlangi, a violent gust of typhoonal wind blew my gown up around my ears. As my remarkable condition of undress was revealed, there was a shocked gasp among the onlookers – a gaggle of wide-eyed matrons in grass skirts. Some explanation was clearly demanded and a sudden inspiration came to my rescue. Through an interpreter I hastily pointed out that these were the undergarments prescribed by custom to be worn by the King Emperor, himself, for the State Opening of Parliament. At other times, I added, loyal subjects could view them on public display in the Tower of London.

My words were received with cheers of approval.

'Kaliba, kaliba,' the crowd chanted. 'Well done sir, well done.'

Meanwhile, Baron Parkhurst had moved on to another theme. 'Tradition,' he declaimed 'must not lead to inflexibility. There must be a willingness to improvise. To be open to change must be part of our legal system. After all,' he went on, 'justice does not begin at 10 am and end at 5 pm.'

The noble baron could not have put it better. Service round the clock had always been my own particular motto. More than once I had been roused in the middle of the night by some legal crisis or another and, only quite recently, PC Josefa had arrived at my bedside flashing a carbide bicycle-lamp through the mosquito net.

A Law for All Seasons

'Urgent writ of Habeus Corpus needed,' he whispered hoarsely. It seemed that Mr Sang Yee Joy, the Chinese store-keeper, was the corpus in question. He had sent a bill to the Headman of the village, Mosese Rambukawaika, for two years' supply of rum. The Headman had promptly locked him in the village privy. Now his brother Chang was indignantly demanding a court order for his release.

'Administer the usual Chinese oath,' I instructed.

Josefa struck a match while Chang, a wrinkled mandarin-figure in a black silk jacket, repeated the necessary words. 'If I speak falsely may my soul be extinguished as this flame.'

Unfortunately, the flame was far from extinguished. As the match dropped to the ground the edge of my mosquito net had caught alight. Mr Chang was quick off the mark with a bucket of water which was standing nearby to catch the drips from my leaking roof. (My complaint to the Public Works Department about the state of my quarters had been ignored for the last six months.) The fire was doused but my predicament was not at an end. Struggling to free myself from the sodden netting I somehow got my arms and legs completely entangled, worsening the situation by trying to force my head through one of the holes.

'Judge is like fly trapped in spider's web,' observed Josefa, beaming the light down upon me with interest. 'Just like in the movies.'

My Orderly was an inveterate patron of the local Hibiscus Cinema.

'Your lordship has seen the film?' he went on enthusiastically. 'It is called *The Fly*. Excellent horror movie.'

'I don't think this is the time or the place for a film review,' I snapped. 'Kindly help me out.'

'I remember film also,' Mr Chang told Josefa animatedly, as the two of them wrestled with the folds of the netting.

'Man is turned into fly and caught by great spider,' he continued for my benefit. 'Velly first-rate show, your honour.'

As I sat up between them a last blackened fragment of netting descended over my face.

'Now lordship is in purdah veil!' chuckled Mr Chang.

'Like wife of Mr Registrar Sharma,' Josefa added.

At this punchline both my visitors doubled up with mirth.

Looking back now I can see the funny side of it, I must admit, although it certainly did not amuse me at the time.

Once again I felt a sharp dig in the ribs, bringing me back to Middle Temple Hall. Baron Parkhurst's peroration seemed to have come to an end. The applause died away into silence.

'Your turn,' Austin Bolsover hissed in my ear.

My turn? What on earth was he talking about?

'Didn't anyone tell you? As the Junior Judge at the dinner it's the custom for you to make the reply.'

All eyes turned on me. For a moment, panic swept over me. Then suddenly I took hold of myself. Perhaps my chance to put the record straight had fortuitously arrived. Here, surely, was a golden opportunity to enlighten this ignorant and complacent audience. At last I could tell them exactly what it was really like to have the awesome responsibility of bearing the burden of British justice in the furthest outposts of Empire.

'A Law for All Seasons,' I began with some deliberation. 'I wonder how many of you gentlemen in your comfortable metropolitan courts have any conception of the hazards of holding court in the outer fringes of darkest Melanesia ... the appalling heat and savage downpour of the monsoon in Fatu-ka-liva . . . facing the spears of the jurymen in a primitive tribal meeting-house . . . I well remember the knotty legal problems posed by the Crown versus Tui-Naviti-Jevu, the notorious forger of shell money . . .'

Perhaps I got a little carried away.

I do seem to recall Baron Parkhurst being helped out to relieve himself as I reached one of my peak moments. Much later on, there were perhaps a few gaps in the surrounding tables. No doubt some guests had trains to catch.

Bolsover told me afterwards that it was, by far, the longest speech on record at a Middle Temple Judges' Dinner. At least, I assured myself, I had achieved that particular niche in the annals of English legal history.

Chapter Eleven

A Highly Indecorous Experience

M Y LEAVE WAS OVER. Back on the treadmill again, I sometimes wondered if my efforts to maintain law and order in the islands were sufficiently appreciated. All too often it struck me that my cooperation was taken for granted, especially when it came to problems of political sensitivity – the latest Pennington crisis, for example.

Even though I was the one who had to act in the matter, nobody had bothered to hold a prior discussion with me. The first I knew about it was when I happened to be consulting, as I frequently did, a reference book on the interpretation of Pacific Colonial Statutes by Professor Berrington Took. This standard work was always kept on the shelf just outside my Chief Justice's room.

I was certainly not eavesdropping, but Sir Neville invariably kept his room open to the breeze and I could not avoid overhearing his telephone conversation. From his deferential tone I knew he must be speaking to the Governor himself.

'I can easily spare Knox Mawer,' Sir Neville was saying. 'That goes without saying, of course,' he added with a grim chuckle.

The CJ must have noticed the glint of my spectacles in the gap between the hinges of his door that had been eaten away by tropical wood-beetles. Anyway, he put down the receiver pretty swiftly and called me in.

'I've just told HE that you'd be delighted to go to Bai Lalevu,' he told me.

'I don't think I know where that is, sir,' I demurred.

'I think you know the Resident Commissioner there, alright!'

He smiled meaningfully.

'Not Pennington, sir?' I began.

'Yes, your old friend J.S. Pennington, it most certainly is.'

I swallowed hard.

'Bai Lalevu happens to be on the outer fringe of his present patch. He's having fresh trouble with some of the islanders there now.'

'Er – how exactly do I come into the picture?'

'He doesn't say exactly. Just that he needs "to borrow a judge", as he puts it. No doubt he'll fill you in when you get there. Not to worry.' Knowing J.S. Pennington, that was easier said than done. However, duty called, and at least Baihalevu would be a change of scene. All I knew about it was that it was a remote, copra-producing atoll, to the west of Samoa.

When the captain of the schooner landed me there, the broken-down wooden jetty under the palm trees was entirely deserted.

'I'll collect you on my way back from Pago-Pago in three days time,' the skipper told me, above the rattle of the anchor chain.

'Where on earth is Pennington?' I asked myself, scanning the surrounding plantation for some sort of human activity. It began to rain heavily and I took shelter in an old copra shed. The humidity inside, combined with the sickly smell of dried coconuts, was overpowering.

Even as I shook out my umbrella there was an ominous rustling from the coconut-husks underfoot. The next moment I found myself confronted by one of the South Pacific's most unpleasant forms of insect life – the red-back, Samoan bully-ant, notorious for its sharp bite and unpleasant side-effects. I tried stamping on one or two of them. Then, to be on the safe side, I hauled myself onto a loading-shelf. Suddenly, the door was flung back against me.

'Where did they go?' demanded a familiar voice. It was J.S. Pennington, all six foot four inches of him, craggy and grizzled in rolled-up khaki shorts and a soiled pith-helmet.

'They're all over the place,' I explained.

He flung open the shutter and peered outside.

'Could be dangerous. Some of them still go for the head, you know,' he said.

I ran my hands through my hair. 'They don't look quite that lethal,' I said.

'What exactly *did* they look like?' he asked.

Bending down, I gingerly held out a dead ant for inspection.

'Like this,' I said.

With an exasperated snort Pennington dashed the specimen to the ground.

'For God's sake!' he exploded. 'This is no time for insect collecting! I'm talking about the Tika-tika.'

The Tika-tika? Was this another form of predatory life, special to Bai Lalevu?

'One of the rebel tribes,' he went on testily. 'Gone back to their head-hunting ways, I'm afraid.'

'Is that what the trouble's about?' I asked faintly. 'You want me to hold some sort of trial?'

A Highly Indecorous Experience

'Not exactly.' Pennington perched himself on a copra-barrel, opened his rucksack and took out a half-full bottle of whisky. Removing the cork with a flourish, he flung it outside into the dripping undergrowth. 'That's something we won't be needing again.' He rummaged through the bag again and brought out a George V Coronation mug.

'Always carry this about with me. Gives one a certain status, if you know what I mean!'

He poured me a generous measure, then helped himself to a swig from the bottle.

'All that matters is that you've brought your regalia with you,' he went on.

I nodded.

'But I wish you'd tell me what I've come to do.'

'All in good time. Tell me' – he leaned back, expansively, while taking another swig – 'what's the news in the capital? Has Old Buffy Harcourt managed to mend the flag-pole at the Polo Club yet?'

J.S. was referring to the occasion when he'd succeeded, during a reckless chukka, in bringing down the Union Jack on the head of the Governor. I was doing my best to bring him up to date with all this, and the rest of the gossip from HQ, when there was a loud snoring alongside me. J.S. was fast asleep. He had a knack of taking a cat-nap during moments of crisis.

A minute later he jerked awake and announced it was time to go. In that part of the tropics, night falls quickly and it was almost dark as we made our way round the headland in the direction of the Government Rest House. Halfway round, we passed some kind of encampment. A signboard outside read World Health Organisation, Family Planning Division.

A stately lady in nursing uniform appeared at the entrance of one of the tents, a lantern in her hand.

93

A Case of Bananas

'Evening, Sister,' roared Pennington.

'Mrs Gertrude Weatherby,' he explained. 'Wonderful woman. Just arrived to teach the islanders about birth control. All the usual contraceptive items and so on. Could prove the answer to everything. If the population went down there'd be plenty of land for everybody.' He swerved at a sharp bend, narrowly missing a pair of Tahitian geese. 'The trouble is persuading them to give it a try.'

J.S. braked the landrover violently, tumbling me out on the steps of the Rest House. This was a shanty affair, even more primitive than his own bungalow back in Numea.

'Welcome to our little B and B,' he said as he showed me to my dingy quarters.

'Extra charge if you *don't* have a bath, I always say.'

He gave one of those rasping barks that indicated he'd made a joke. 'That copra-pong certainly hangs around, if you don't mind my saying.'

The water in the Rest House ablutions was decidedly brackish. I was doing my best with the aid of a large pumice stone when Pennington rattled the door.

'Don't be put off by the colour of the flow,' he called. 'One of the pigs fell into the tank yesterday, but it didn't seem to do her permanent harm.'

J.S. moved off, humming tunelessly.

'Let the bubbles of the mind float to the surface,' he called back. Lying back in the rust-encrusted cauldron this wasn't exactly easy. I was out in a trice, rubbed myself down and emerged for dinner on the verandah. Batu, the cook, a bandy-legged midget with a fanatical devotion to J.S., had produced two of his master's favourite dishes – goat curry, and a rugby-sized breadfruit, well charred in the earth oven. Spotted dick was to follow, steamed in a length of barkcloth.

A Highly Indecorous Experience

'English people like this dish,' he informed me proudly, bearing aloft the enormous suet roll studded with dried paw-paw. It was a good thing my trusty medicine-chest was to hand, with the rest of my luggage.

'Think I'll get an early night,' I told Pennington as Batu cleared away.

'Quite right,' said my host. 'Big day tomorrow.'

When I reported for breakfast I found Pennington sitting in a bright yellow kimono at the dining-table. It had nothing on it save for a bottle of gin and two glasses. He motioned for me to sit down and poured a neat measure to match his own. I managed to dispose of this in a potted fern behind my chair. Pennington placed the bottle in the kitchen cupboard and then disappeared to dress. I was furtively investigating the cupboard in search of food when Pennington returned.

'Do you mind if –' I began.

'By all means, help yourself.'

He brought out the gin again.

'Though, generally, I find one's enough at this time of the morning,' he added in a tone of faint reproof.

'No, no,' I demurred. 'I thought perhaps a spot of something to eat, a bean or two perhaps.'

'Ah, yes,' said J.S. 'The best of Mr Heinz's 57 Varieties, eh?'

He removed a rusty dagger from the wall, a relic of his early days among the Bedouin tribes of British Arabia, and plunged it into the nearest can.

'Eat up,' he said, passing me the weapon.

The operation was a delicate one but I managed a couple of mouthfuls without serious injury. Then Pennington sat down, 'to explain things', as he put it.

'The root of the trouble is land,' he said. 'As the years go by there just isn't enough to go round. As you've gathered already we're seriously over-populated and

95

now they've taken to fighting about it.'

I spiked another baked bean and tried to concentrate upon J.S.'s usual grasshopper style of imparting information.

'Even so,' he went on, 'come what may, in the past, I could always rely upon Charlie Ponsomby to help me keep the lid on things.'

Charlie Ponsomby? I knew that my Victorian predecessor, Judge Charlie Ponsomby, had done pioneering work in these particular islands. Indeed, he had brought about what is known in colonial history as Ponsomby's Peace. But the man had been dead for ninety years. So what on earth was Pennington rambling on about?

'Last year's tidal wave,' said J.S., 'that was the last straw.'

'Tidal wave?' I said, now completely lost.

'It was the very first breaker of the lot. Simply swept up the beach and removed old Ponsomby from his post for good and all.'

'Removed him from his post?'

At this point Pennington completely lost patience with me.

'For heaven's sake, Knox Mawer, do you have to repeat everything I say?'

There was a silence for the moment as he watched my futile efforts to scoop up the last of the sauce from the bottom of the tin.

'Why not up end the damn thing and be done with it!'

I did as I was told.

'I'm sorry if I don't seem to understand,' I said, removing my spectacles to clean off the remains of the beans.

'It's perfectly simple,' J.S. expostulated. 'Surely you know all about Charlie Ponsomby?'

I blinked.

A Highly Indecorous Experience

'Well, when he finally left Bai Lalevu Ponsomby presented the elders with his wig,' continued J.S. 'It had always fascinated them. They thought it was the secret of his *mana*, his power. From then on it was kept in front of the tribal meeting-house – a sort of Shrine to Peace, if you follow. *Kavaduduvo* it was called.'

'I'm afraid my knowledge of the language isn't –' I began.

'The nearest you'd get in English,' J.S. interjected, 'would be Great White Thinking Cap.'

I nodded slowly.

'So my job is to think out a solution to their present troubles. Pick up where Ponsomby left off, so to speak. I see.'

It was a moment for careful reflection.

'At least,' I assured J.S., 'where traditional land disputes are in question, you'll not find me short of expertise.'

'Never mind the expertise, dear boy,' said J.S. 'This time it's appearances that count. You've brought your usual gear with you, I'm glad to observe.'

Somewhat bemused, I watched as J.S. issued an order to Batu. The faithful midget proceeded to load my regalia into the back of his master's landrover with the black and gold wig box (from Ede & Ravenscroft, Chancery Lane) on top.

'We'll go straight to the *locus in quo*,' Pennington announced. He drew on a pair of ancient driving gauntlets and sprang to the wheel. Within seconds we were bumping along the southern coast road which led to the main village. I could see reminders of the tidal wave everywhere. Several of the bures, or thatched huts, were in ruins. There was no sign of rebuilding, however, and most of the villagers seemed to be engaged in sharpening spears ready for the next sortie against their neighbours. At the centre of the village green was a kind of totem pole rather like a rudimentary version of Cleopatra's needle.

'That's where they hung Ponsomby's wig,' J.S. explained. 'Placed it on top for all to behold.'

He glanced at my baggage meaningfully.

'Look here, J.S.,' I said, catching on, 'that wig of mine cost £200 at least.'

'Don't worry. I'll speak to Sir Neville and you'll be reimbursed.'

Groups of islanders were now viewing our arrival with interest.

'Well, what do you want me to do next, exactly?'

'Just open up the wig-box.'

The islanders pressed about, chattering excitedly.

'Right,' said J.S., 'put it on.'

I must say I felt rather silly donning my full-bottom and standing there in my shorts, but the roar of delight that went up reassured me.

Pennington broke into a long peroration in their local tongue. I assumed he must be explaining that I was some kind of judicial reincarnation of Charles Ponsomby. The next minute his hand swept the wig off my head and replaced it in the Ede & Ravenscroft box.He beckoned the elderly Chief and handed it over to him with a bow. There was a round of applause as, grinning from ear to ear, the old gentleman firmly sat down on it.

We had to leave before the actual installation, since the tide was coming in over the coastal track. But as we moved off I began to feel that, after all, it had been a job well done. No doubt the islanders would now settle down to a general armistice.

I returned by schooner to base and, about a week later, Sir Neville sent for me. He looked quite pleased.

A Highly Indecorous Experience

'Had a letter from Pennington,' he said. 'There's every sign that your visit was a success. Seems the islanders have reached a kind of *modus vivendi* at last. The future looks bright, you might say.'

I felt a glow of satisfaction. In my mind's eye I saw the reference to 'Knox Mawer's Peace' in the colonial history books.

'So the old wig did the trick, then? Watching over things at the top of the totem pole, just like Judge Ponsomby's?'

Sir Neville paused.

'Your wig is back in position,' he agreed.

He cleared his throat.

'However, it's not exactly a totem pole, you know. What you saw was the classic phallic symbol of the ancient Polynesian type. Part of the Easter Island giant worshipping tradition.'

'I see.'

'Apparently, the people of Bai Lalevu, including the Tika-tika tribe, have got things a bit mixed up.'

He coughed again.

'Your arrival coincided with Sister Weatherby and her family planning campaign, if you understand me.'

'I'm afraid I don't, sir.'

Sir Neville began to shuffle some files in front of him. He seemed at a loss for words.

'Perhaps if I tell you the new name they've given for your wig it might help to put you in the picture.'

'What is the new name, sir?'

I had rather liked the idea of a Great White Thinking Cap.

Sir Neville still refused to meet my gaze.

'*Kavaduduvu ni-samo-drakundrove*,' he said rapidly.

'I'm afraid I'm not as much on the mark on the meaning of the Bulalevu dialect as you are, Sir Neville,' I said, as he showed me to the door.

'Er – exact translation is difficult,' he stalled.

Then relenting, he took a deep breath and said with a note of finality, 'Put simply it means The Great White Condom.'

Recovering myself back in Chambers I started to make out an order for a replacement wig. Reasons for Loss of Previous Wig the form demanded. With a sigh of resignation I began to set out the details, then stopped. Carefully I crossed out what I had written, ticking, instead, just 'Official Misunderstanding'.

Even for Ede & Ravenscroft, Purveyors of Judicial Regalia since George III was King, it really was too long a story. Or too tall a one perhaps. But then, they had never met J.S. Pennington.

Chapter Twelve

A Footnote
in Legal History

FOR AS LONG as I had known him, Mr Sharma had
been engaged upon a monumental work of legal
scholarship. An ambitious project, it was entitled *Lives
of the Judges: A Biographical Dictionary of Great Men of
the Bench from the Sixteenth to the Twentieth Centuries
Inclusive.*

Modelled after the style of Dr Johnson's *Lives of the
Poets*, this work, in Mr Sharma's eyes, was to win him a
unique place in legal literature. Regrettably, the learned
Registrar seemed to progress ever more slowly upon the
project.

'Writer's block,' he would frequently complain, looking up from his desk where he sat with a damp towel
round his head. His stacks of material seemed to grow
higher by the month. The whole of his spare time was
spent making notes in the Suba Law Library, crouched
at the dusty bottom shelves, labelled Biography. His
jottings, tabulated into a number of ever-expanding
files, were stored for some curious reason in wicker
laundry-baskets behind the fire extinguisher.

'For security reasons,' as Mr Sharma once explained
to me. An inveterate teacher, he was constantly lectur-

ing me about judges of the past who stood particularly high in his esteem. Not surprisingly, he had a special interest in those who had served in different parts of the Empire.

The name of Sir Mathew Begbie, for instance, was frequently on his lips. An enormous statue of Sir Mathew, the first Chief Justice of British Columbia, stood outside Parliament Buildings, Victoria, and Mr Sharma had once taken a package trip to Canada to see the great man for himself.

'I climbed up on to his knee,' he reported, 'to take a photograph at close quarters.'

He showed me a photograph of a gigantic marble waistcoat with a hint of whiskers above it.

'Alas, a Mountie on duty there pulled me down at the critical moment or the result would have been more successful.'

Mr Sharma had a strong sense of drama and liked, wherever possible, to re-enact the pronouncements of his favourite judges. This he did in the style of an old-fashioned ventriloquist, switching the dialogue from one side of his mouth to the other. An occasion when Sir Mathew was about to pass sentence upon a trapper, convicted of murder, was one of his favourite re-enactments.

'Have you anything to say before judgment is pronounced?' Mr Sharma would rasp, in the imagined tones of Chief Justice Begbie, puffing out his cheeks and baring his teeth. Turning on his heel, he then took up the stance of the defendant cowering in the dock.

'Yes, Judge Begbie. I want to appeal to the Colonial Secretary in London.' Here Mr Sharma about-turned and adopted again the menacing scowl of the judge.

'Certainly my man. It will, of course, take six months for the Colonial Secretary to deal with the matter. But his decision will be of little interest to you since you are to be hanged next Monday morning.'

Mr Sharma rolled his head from side to side appreciatively.

'What wit that great man had!'

'Sounds appalling to me,' I said.

'In those early days it was necessary for justice to be swift.'

'Well, we're certainly getting behind with it here,' I put in sharply. 'Mrs Chu-Sang has been waiting to post up your Daily Cause List on the noticeboard for over thirty minutes!'

However, once started on Sir Mathew Begbie, nothing would stop Mr Sharma. Darting into my secretary's cubby-hole with the List he was back again, almost without drawing breath.

'Have I ever related the case of the Yankee cowboy, the one convicted of assault before Sir Mathew?'

'You have,' I sighed. But Mr Sharma, his eyes glittering, was already locked into character again.

Sir Mathew I shall fine you 100 dollars.
Prisoner Why, that's dandy, judge, I got that in ma breech-pocket.
Sir Mathew And six months' imprisonment with hard labour. Maybe you've got that in your other pocket!

There was a pause while Mr Sharma looked round an invisible court-room for laughter and applause. Fortunately, at that moment, the sound of the tipstaff's handbell interruped him and it was time to take up my own seat of justice once again.

Drawing on his store of judicial anecdotes, Mr Sharma was like one of those revolving Victorian desk-calendars with an apt quotation for every day. On the morning, for example, when a leading article in the

A Case of Bananas

Planters Gazette criticized the sentence I had passed upon an embezzler (who happened to be the brother-in-law of the Editor), Mr Sharma was quick to console me.

'Remember the words of Lord Chancellor Bacon,' he said. 'Nothing is as much to be abhorred as a popular judge.'

I tried to make the best of this piece of wisdom especially since, at the same time, I was dealing with another *cause célèbre*. Seamus O'Brien, a red-headed newcomer to the island judiciary, had got more than usually drunk and fired a shot-gun through the lavatory window of the house of the Police Commissioner when that gentleman was using the facility. He claimed he had done it for a bet on the Irish Sweepstake with Father O'Malley of the Little Sisters of St Joseph Mission. His letter of apology to the Commissioner was profuse and picturesque, describing himself as just a playboy of the Western world with no harm done. Nevertheless, I was obliged to arrange for his return ticket to Dublin.

'It is a most lenient arrangement compared to Tudor times,' Mr Sharma pointed out. 'When Justiciar Fitzgerald fell out of favour in 1597, he too was deported back to his native land. But he was required to walk barefoot from the Tower of London to get there.'

'All the way across the Irish Sea?' I queried, throwing a dash of cold water on the story.

'There was a boat waiting for him at Fishguard,' Mr Sharma replied with dignity. His historical detail could never be faulted.

As a result of Mr O'Brien's departure my own case-load was heavier than usual. Mr Sharma was constantly urging speed upon me as we worked our way through the list. He even took to timing each case, something I found particularly irritating. I had been taking a little

104

trouble to explain the meaning of a Community Service Order to a persistent young hooligan. Passing through the Library at lunchtime I came across the Registrar going through the contents of his laundry-basket marked Nineteenth Century.

'Trial before Hawkins J, reported in Cox's Pleas of the Crown 1866, is the shortest case on record,' he read out. 'All the judge said to the prisoner was "We have met before, Jones, we shall not meet again. Transportation for life. Next case."'

Mr Sharma tapped his watch.

'Twelve seconds flat. That is what we need to aim for.' He returned his notes to the basket and sat down cross-legged to compose himself for his usual midday Yoga session.

Mr Sharma's adages were not, however, directed exclusively at me. 'You are obviously not acquainted with *Speculum Juris*,' he once told Emu Buksh, a particularly discourteous local advocate.

'I have never met such a person,' said Mr Buksh.

Mr Sharma flashed open his pocket-book.

'It is the well-known *Sixteenth-Century Advice to Advocates* by Guillaume Durand,' quoted the Registrar. '"When the judge speaks, the wise lawyer listens respectfully then praises his lordship's wisdom."'

Mr Buksh had the grace to take the piece of chewing-gum out of his mouth and place it in his handkerchief before resuming his defence of a well-known receiver of stolen ukuleles.

In dealing with such rogues Mr Sharma considered me altogether too restrained.

'Remember the words of the poet, John Skelton, on Lord Chancellor Wolsey,' he chided. 'He rages and he raves, And calls them cankered knaves.'

'Most undignified,' I said.

A Case of Bananas

'And it was always said of Lord Justice Scroggs in court that it was like hearing the bellowing of a wild bull.'

He shook his head ruefully.

'Such colourful characters! I'm afraid those days are gone.'

'What about our own Judge Hoskyn-Boggis?' I countered. 'He used to sit with a squawking pet parrot on the Bench.'

Mr Sharma was unimpressed. I tried again, reminding him of the famous Chancery Judge, Lord Clare. He used to have a labrador alongside him in court. One day the judge seemed to be paying more attention to the dog than to the case so, after a few minutes, counsel sat down. 'Get on with it,' snapped Lord Clare. Counsel retorted with a deep bow to the dog. 'Beg pardon,' he observed, 'I thought your lordships were in consultation!'

Mr Sharma did not react.

'It was a joke, Mr Sharma.'

'I see no humour in having an unclean animal in such a position,' he replied.

'At least it was better than bats,' I said.

I was thinking of my recent visit to Yailoma where the flying foxes were regarded as the sacred ancestors of the ruling family. There was no odour of sanctity about their roosting places. One of these included the thatched roof of the court-house. After some argument I had ruled out Mr Sharma's plan to sprinkle the place with vinegar, a method used, according to his researches, in the Court of the Star Chamber. All the same, the Registrar had not taken kindly to making do with the Penang Fumigation Pump from the Army and Navy Stores that accompanied me on all my travels.

'What is wrong with tradition?' he grumbled, a familiar remark of his.

A Footnote in Legal History

'Nothing at all,' I said, 'but isn't there anyone from our own twentieth century in whom you are especially interested?'

'Broomfield,' he replied mysteriously.

I had never heard the name but he was apparently famous in Mr Sharma's native India.

'The late Mr Justice Broomfield was the judge who tried Gandhi for sedition. As you know, the Mahatma was always against violence. Unhappily, his speeches led to rioting so he was charged and sent to prison. But at the end of the trial the judge said a very remarkable thing. "If the course of events in this country make it possible for you, Mr Gandhi, to be released a free man, then nobody will be better pleased than I."' Here Mr Sharma blew his nose emotionally.

'A man of much wisdom,' he commented. 'He knew he was dealing with a man of destiny. He was able to take the larger view of history.'

As usual, Mr Sharma seemed to be laying down guidelines for my own performance on the Bench. A bit unnecessary this time, I thought. I was hardly likely to encounter a man of destiny in the atolls of Micronesia. That was before Mosese Benibokasi appeared on the scene.

At first Mosese seemed to be no more than a religious fanatic. A Neanderthal figure in a long white night shirt he was regularly seen parading up and down the market-place with a banner of coconut matting announcing the end of the world. On the back was a message urging people to eat only bananas and abstain from sexual intercourse. Local elections were due and Mosese offered himself as the Marxist candidate for Nabongi-bongi.

Soon afterwards, he began to preach civil disobedience, calling for the non-payment of land-tax. Trouble broke out and he was charged with promoting an affray. Adopting the Broomfield approach I told the defendant that, on account of his age, I would place him on probation, provided he signed an undertaking to be of good behaviour. He shook his head. The end of the world, he insisted, was due a week on Wednesday. Until then it was his duty to carry on spreading the word against wrongdoing, private and public.

'Meanwhile, I shall lie in jail.'

He left the court defiantly singing what sounded like the German National Anthem. I remanded him for a report by Dr Arnold Mann, the Chief Medical Officer who also claimed a qualification in psychiatry. Unfortunately, this provided Dr Mann with a golden opportunity to settle a ridiculous personal vendetta against me. After all, it was not my fault if twice, in recent weeks, my Morris Minor had had to be left obstructing his official space in the Government car park while Vishnu Sharma did his best to repair a persistent oil leak. A younger brother of the Registrar, he was a willing breakdown mechanic, but tended to take his time while puzzling out the difference between the cylinder-head and the radiator.

'This prisoner is suffering from no delusions of any sort,' reported Dr Mann, to my dismay.

Mosese continued to remain adamant. He still refused to sign the bond. 'I am waiting for the first sign,' he insisted. 'It will come with the moving of the ground. Soon after, the earth will yield up the dead.'

'I see, Mr Banibokasi,' I said.

I remanded the case again. Feelings began to run high. It seemed I was going to have a political martyr on my hands. Court was reassembled with the Public Gallery jammed. Just as we appeared to have reached another stalemate a distinct vibration could be felt under our feet. That morning the Public Works Department had begun to sink a new drain beneath the court-house. There was a cavernous rumble, then another.

'The earth moves!' cried Mosese.

I did not contradict him.

'The sign has come. My work is done.' He was beaming from ear to ear.

'You will sign the bond then, Mosese?' I asked.

Mosese took up the pen.

'I shall put my name to the paper then go home to prepare myself.'

This was greeted with a round of applause. I too felt a wave of relief as Mosese left the court and I was able to turn to run-of-the-mill cases.

Later that day, however, I noticed that Mr Sharma had the laundry-basket labelled Twentieth Century at his side and was scribbling briskly.

'Something new you've discovered, Mr Sharma?' I enquired politely.

'I am summarizing this morning's proceedings for inclusion in my *Lives*,' he said.

'How very gratifying, Mr Sharma,' I said.

He carefully replaced his Swan fountain-pen among the battery of other pens and propelling-pencils clipped to his top pocket.

'As a footnote, of course,' he added.

'Naturally,' I replied.

When had I ever been anything else?

Chapter Thirteen

Desert Island Discs

RECLINING ON THE PROW of the *Sawaika Supreme Court* launch with the trade wind in my face and Bracton's *Dictionary of Legal Phraseology* on my knees, what more could a man want, I asked myself? I was on circuit amongst the islands of Saiwaika. 'Days of heavenly brightness sparkling with the dust of diamonds,' was how Robert Louis Stevenson had described his voyaging in this part of Polynesia. Stevenson was roaming the Pacific in search of an island home. Before him, the missionaries were landing on these shores bringing the heathen into the light of Christianity. Perhaps it was not too fanciful to say that, in my small way, I too had a destiny to fulfil in this remote area of the world. After all, I was bringing to the Polynesians, in place of the club and spear, the inestimable boon of English Common Law, a unique system of justice fashioned by centuries of learned precedent.

With a sigh of satisfaction I took a refreshing sip of Andrews Liver Salts and turned the page to 'Causation' and 'Chance-Medley'. Behind me, at the wheel, stood Josefa, my Orderly, alert and forever reliable. Earlier that morning he had asked me to read to him from my book. It was not considered polite in Polynesian society to keep a good story to oneself.

Desert Island Discs

'What did this *tusitala*, this teller of tales, have to say?' he enquired. 'He must know many legends for the book to be so long and heavy.'

I had done my best. Perhaps I could explain some of the Latin maxims, cited in Bracton, by using local illustrations.

'*Nemo dat quod non habet*,' I began. 'In other words, Josefa, if you've mortgaged your coconut plantation to the bank you can only pass it on to your son with the money still owing upon it.'

Josefa nodded politely.

'*Volenti non fit injuria*,' I went on. I paused to rack my brains and had a flash of inspiration.

'No wrong would be done, Josefa, to your hero Mosese Winibokasi, the wrestling champion of Tonga, should he be injured in a match to which he had agreed. He cannot make a legal complaint against his opponent in those circumstances.'

I tried to compress the next two pages into some kind of colloquial language. Quite successfully, I thought. But when I looked up, Josefa had fallen asleep at the wheel.

There were startled cries as we narrowly missed a passing canoe. I suggested it was time for some refreshment and handed him an orange from my picnic-basket. With some interest I noticed he threw the final segment of the fruit over the rail into the waves.

'Just to thank Manoa, the Shark God, for a lucky escape,' he explained. 'He is the ancestor of my tribe and these are his waters.'

Back at the helm Josefa was humming to himself some ancient island chant – or was it a favourite Wesleyan hymn? Suddenly there came a ghastly crunching noise from the stern and we lurched to an abrupt halt.

111

A Case of Bananas

The singing stopped.

'Boat all fucked up, my lord,' called Josefa.

There was little point in rebuking the good lad for an innocent repetition of something overheard at the more uncouth end of the Planters Club Bar. Especially when I had an obvious crisis on my hands. I peered over the edge. There was no doubt about it. The *Saiwaika Supreme Court* was stuck upon the Saiwaika Reef!

'Looks as if your Shark God doesn't like oranges, Josefa,' I remarked with some exasperation.

Already, the water was rising around my ankles. In a trice I took charge of the situation. There was more grinding and this time the engine came to a full stop.

'Bail out,' I said, handing Josefa a bucket. This was no time to stand upon ceremony. Removing my wig from its container I put the black and gold Ede & Ravenscroft box to a novel use. We worked hard but to no avail.

'Take off ballast,' I called. 'Without further delay.'

First to go overboard was a heavy load of confiscated firearms, mainly old muzzle loaders which I had impounded at the sessions held back at Naiseriloma. 'It's Government property,' I reminded Josefa, 'so a detailed inventory will be required by Mr Harold Took, the official auditor.'

We were now several hundredweight lighter. Even so, the boat still refused to budge, despite Josefa's efforts with a sculling pole. He dived underneath to assess the damage. Apparently, the stern had come to rest upon a coral ledge.

'For heaven's sake, don't get rid of that court safe before I remove the contents,' I said. Our predicament was no excuse for relaxing departmental requirements of this kind, not where Mr Took was concerned.

Anxiously we scanned the horizon. With luck there might be an outrigger, fishing for an early morning catch. However, all that could be seen was a strip of sand with a solitary palm tree some 200 yards north of our position – clearly an uninhabited atoll which had never been charted on the map.

'Why not let me take the raft back to Naiseriloma for the relief launch?' suggested Josefa.

The raft in question was a frail bamboo structure used to load fruit and only large enough to support one person.

It was good thinking. Like all Pacific folk Josefa was no stranger to the age-old skills of ocean navigation.

'First, I shall make your lordship safe on dry land,' he said.

Perched on his shoulders as he waded ashore I was landed there in next to no time. It was touching to see that he had also carried the volume of Bracton with him to lay at my feet.

Standing alone on the beach watching Josefa paddle away into the blue, I had to admit to a momentary qualm. There was little shade to be found. Even stripped to my trousers, I found the noonday sun hard to take. Some form of protection might alleviate an aching head and prevent more burning on those parts of the scalp where the hair was thin. Luckily, my string vest provided me with a crude turban.

'Sinbad the sailor!' I chuckled.

At least I could still see the funny side of things.

'Marooned on a desert island!'

I threw myself down amongst a patch of pandanus reed and imagined Roy Plomley's voice in my ear.

'What records should I choose?' I enquired of a sea-gull on a nearby rock.

I had always retained happy memories of the show *Rosemarie* since I was taken to see it on Brighton Pier by

Aunt Sylvia at an early age.

'When I'm calling you – oo – oo – oo – oo – oo – oo,' I began.

The seagull took to the air.

Something a bit more solid perhaps? Elgar's 'Land of Hope and Glory' for instance. I tried again. Somehow, that one needed a full orchestra behind it.

'And a favourite book?' the voice continued.

No problem there. Not with my *Dictionary of Legal Phraseology* to hand.

'How would you while away the time?'

This was easy. I had already started to build a sand-castle. Well, not exactly a castle, rather a working model of my ideal Supreme Court for the South Pacific. I had got as far as the grand staircase and must have become quite carried away with the operation. Tired out, I fell into a heavy sleep among the reeds.

I was aroused by the sound of shuffling feet and a startled gasp.

'Someone's here, Merle!' called a shrill female voice, an American.

'Be careful!'

'Land's sakes!' rejoined another. 'And our captain said these darned beachcombers were extinct nowadays!'

'Poor man,' squeaked another voice. 'Not a stitch on, save for them ragged britches. Not even a roof over his head.'

Half hidden by the reeds, I thought it best to continue to feign sleep. There was a clicking of cameras. This was really too much. Rubbing my eyes I scrambled to my feet and found myself surrounded by what was clearly a party of tourists – ladies in floral dresses and sunglasses with stout canvas shoes on their feet. I caught a glimpse of Captain Withers's *Blue Lagoon* pleasure cruiser from Saiwaika, anchored offshore.

'Hello, old timer,' called one of them. 'Don't be frightened.'

'Perhaps we're the first white faces he's seen in years,' whispered another of the visitors. 'Just like Robinson Crusoe!'

'Sorry to disappoint you,' I interrupted. It was high time to put the record straight.

I was removing my turban with as much dignity as possible when I noticed Josefa sprinting up towards us from around the headland.

'And here's Man Friday,' quipped a lady photographer. 'Could you two just stand together for another snap, please.'

I cleared my throat.

'I happen to be one of Her Majesty's circuit judges, Madam,' I announced, rolling down my trouser leg. 'And this is my Orderly, Mr Josefa Naiserlangi.'

There was a stunned silence. All the ladies began talking at once, then drew back a little.

'Castaways have these delusions,' one of them was saying. 'It's mainly due to the isolation.'

Tactfully, Josefa drew me aside. 'Relief launch is around the bay, my lord,' he said. 'We have to hurry to catch the tide.'

Turning upon my heel I strode rapidly away from the tourists. I was only halfway down the beach when one of them came hurrying after us. She was bearing in both hands my volume of Bracton.

'You've left your bible behind, Mister – er – Judge,' she said. She gave a sympathetic smile. 'You wouldn't want to lose that, I guess.'

'You're quite right about this valuable item from my Law Library,' I replied.

A Case of Bananas

I gave her a courtly bow before following Josefa around the headland.

Out in the bay the little cutter was waiting. But even as we clambered aboard, it seemed that a further emergency was about to confront me.

'Radio message for you, sir,' announced the skipper. Through the headphones I heard the muffled accusing tones of Mr Registrar Sharma.

'I did warn you,' he began. 'You should not have gone without me.'

'Yes, yes, Mr Sharma,' I said with some irritation. 'What is it?'

Above the crackle of the radio-waves I caught an all too-familiar sound. Mr Sharma had paused to blow his nose. Must be something up, I realized.

'We have a red-hot case of sedition here, awaiting your urgent attention,' he informed me.

He gave that maddening chuckle of his.

'You may wish you'd stayed on your desert island, after all!'

Chapter Fourteen

The Train of Progress

BY THE TIME I rejoined Mr Sharma back in the capital, his 'red-hot case of sedition' had cooled down. Tomasi Rabuka, President of the Biti Farmers Association, had urged his members to throw a consignment of Agricultural Department coconuts into the lagoon as a symbol of defiance against Government legislation over quality. Happily, all had safely floated back to the beach with the incoming tide and no loss was sustained. The Public Prosecutor withdrew the charge against Tomasi and let him off with a caution.

This left a gap in the Court diary for the next few days, enabling Mr Sharma to put in some more time upon his *Lives of the Judges*. Unfortunately, his persistent habit of reading favourite extracts to me had the same effect on my nerves as a needle stuck in the groove of a cracked gramophone record. So it was a relief to get Chief Justice Sir Neville Gawsby's cable: SET OUT IMMEDIATELY FOR LODONI TO OFFICIALLY OPEN NEW COURT-HOUSE THERE.

Lodoni lay at the heart of the up-country sugar-cane lands, miles from anywhere. A court-house in this remote hinterland for the speedy settlement of local disputes marked an important stage of progress in the Chief Justice's development programme.

. . . a golden opportunity to display his prowess at 'rough-riding'

The Train of Progress

Transport was the immediate problem. The Public Works Department reported that it was six weeks behind schedule with the new road. But Mr Sharma, now on his mettle to impress the CJ with his efficiency, would brook no delay.

'We will make our own arrangements,' he declared.

For him it was a golden opportunity to display his prowess at 'rough-riding' astride his cherished Norton 350 motorbike. He had acquired the machine from the Army Surplus Store in Suba and exercised it regularly as part of his philosophy that 'a healthy mind must inhabit a healthy body'.

As far as I was concerned, the hiring of mules was arranged. Josefa would take the lead mount. A second would carry me. Mr Sharma proposed a third one for the court baggage.

'Surely that can all be accommodated on these two?' I protested, knowing how closely Sir Neville scrutinized every claim for travelling expenses. The Registrar shook his head. He rummaged through the laundry-basket, labelled eighteenth century, and proceeded to cite an extract from a famous exchange of correspondence.

'"James Boswell to Lord Braxfield, Scots Lord of Session (1780),"' Mr Sharma intoned. '"My Lord. Ye full apparatus of pompe doth inspire more reverence and prevente more crimes than thousands of executiones. Do not therefore pinch pennies by abolishing ye baggage-mule by storing ye equipage in ye carriage along with ye boot brushes!" Lord Braxfield in reply. "'Tis Agreed."'

I had no answer to that compelling precedent. A third animal was hired. Upon its back was strapped *Halsbury's Laws of England*, my robing box and the new Lodoni Seal for the stamping of writs.

The first part of the journey was far from comfortable,

particularly when it came to fording the Naisori River, but at least I could feel that, once again, I was following Robert Louis Stevenson whose *Travels with a Donkey* had always been a book I greatly admired.

Regrettably, we had only reached our first staging-post, the small bush-settlement of Riki-Riki, when a hitch arose. I hastened to report over the radio transmitter to Mr Sharma.

'Knox Mawer here,' I began, but it was difficult to get a word in edgeways. Mr Sharma poured out a rapid account of his own 'tip-top journey' on the Norton. He was now ensconced at Lodoni where final preparations were proceeding smoothly.

'The flagpole is correctly positioned and I have already drilled and rehearsed the necessary tribal guard-of-honour. In addition, I have arranged . . .'

'Excuse my interrupting,' I said, 'it's just that I've run into a spot of trouble at my end.'

'Trouble?' snapped the Registrar. 'What trouble?'

'All three mules seem to have gone down with some kind of tetse-fever.'

'No replacements?' he demanded.

'None at all, I'm afraid.'

There was an irascible silence. I could hear his mind working furiously.

'It will have to be the sugar train then,' he announced firmly. 'This very instant I shall ring my wife's cousin who is the Railway Superintendent.'

He replaced the receiver before there was time for further discussion.

It was perfectly true that Riki-Riki was a stopping-point for the single-track waggon train which transported the raw cane from the fields down the valley to the loading wharf. It was hardly likely, I thought, that it was able to carry passengers. However, I decided that at least I could find out what the Railway Superintendent had to say on the subject. Tentatively, I knocked on the door of the corrugated iron shack which constituted the Railway Superintendent's office. Through an open shutter alongside the entrance I was confronted by a white beard of inordinate length.

'Superintendent Ravindra Singh at your service,' said its owner.

'Did Mr Sharma speak to you?' I enquired.

'The Registrar has been in touch. Perhaps your lordship would care to inspect the transport in question?'

He led me out into a siding.

Resting against a fallen palm tree was a miniature locomotive, painted bright yellow with a tall brass funnel. Coupled to it were three small trucks. I peered into one of them and saw a large mound of dried cane stubble.

'I suppose one could make oneself fairly comfortable on top of all that,' I suggested hopefully.

The Superintendent's immense stomach quivered with silent mirth.

'Dear sir. Not the waggons!' he said. 'Thou art no piece of sugar-cane in spite of thine extreme thinness!'

He rocked to and fro, savouring the joke.

'But your lordship is welcome to travel in the driver's cab, as does our company inspector from time to time.'

'Very kind,' I murmured.

The Superintendent brought out from the folds of his turban a small ivory prong and thoughtfully began to comb his beard.

'But, alas, no driver is available at present,' he sighed. 'Industrial action. Protest over cut in midday curry-break.'

Once again I got through to Mr Sharma on the radio transmitter.

A Case of Bananas

'Looks as if the Opening Ceremony will have to be postponed,' I informed him.

'Out of the question,' he snapped. 'It is vital to keep up standards of punctuality in these last days of Empire.'

There was a burst of static as Mr Sharma delivered himself of this favourite maxim of his.

'Besides,' he continued, 'Chief Epeli has arranged a traditional welcome. The sucking pigs are already in the earth ovens. In addition, the Lodoni folk have composed a special *meke* to commemorate the occasion.'

I was, of course, familiar with the Polynesian dance which portrayed memorable events in tribal history, a sort of living archive of folk-lore. I mopped my forehead. It was getting very hot in the Superintendent's tiny shed and my patience was beginning to fray.

'Do you expect the engine to drive itself, Mr Sharma?' I demanded.

'What has happened to the famous British gift of initiative?' enquired the Registrar pointedly.

Looking back, I can see that this was a shrewd way of 'putting me to the test', as it were. After all, I reflected, had not my own Uncle Martin, then manager of the Altrincham high street branch of the Midland Bank, driven the Altrincham Express during the General Strike of 1926? How often had Aunt Sylvia shown me the sepia photograph of Uncle waving cheerily from the cab, amidst clouds of steam, with his young counter-clerk beside him acting as stoker.

'Had no experience whatsoever, your uncle hadn't,' she always said. 'But he managed to get through alright.'

Not that she told the entire truth. There had been a minor explosion in the boiler when he came to Chester. Through an oversight at Beeston Castle Uncle Martin had forgotten to fill up with water. Since not a single passenger had so far ventured aboard, no inconvenience had been caused and the bill for repairs, incurred by the Great Western Railway Company, was eventually settled by the Midland Bank.

I took a grip of myself. Surely I could maintain the family honour by driving this altogether smaller machine? No doubt it was infinitely simpler to manage.

'So long as I can persuade Josefa to do the stoking,' I told Mr Sharma, 'I'll see what can be done.'

Josefa's reaction was a beam of assent as he set off to collect the baggage from the stables. Meanwhile, I hurried back to the bearded Superintendent for instructions.

'I want to be quite clear that this is a practical proposition,' I told him as I swung myself up into the cab.

'The operation, sir, is basically straightforward. Apart from a slight gradient it is smooth going the whole way.'

'But what about the controls?'

'Quite elementary.'

Tucking his beard into his turban, the Superintendent joined me on the footplate.

'Your honour merely operates this lever. It moves in the ratchet thus. In order to accelerate, the wheel is turned in a clockwise direction. Speed is shown here on this dial. There is the whistle, operated, like everythng else, by steam. I would go with you myself but I am required by company regulations never to leave my post.'

As he spoke, Josefa returned with my gear.

'Will your honour be wearing your honour's wig?' he demanded breathlessly. He was eager to get started on this novel venture. 'All the Lodoni people will expect to see you in full regalia, sir,' he insisted.

'Don't be ridiculous,' I said. 'Under the circumstances it would be wholly inappropriate.'

A Case of Bananas

Superintendent Singh backed me up on this. 'You will need to get a big fire going under the boiler, Josefa,' he told him. 'There will be many sparks. We cannot risk the setting alight of his honour's head-piece, can we?'

Josefa pointed out that word had spread through the usual bush-telegraph of my proposed official journey.

'No judge before has driven the sugar train,' he pointed out. 'That is why I am saying the dignity of the law must be upheld.'

'Very well,' I compromised. 'I am prepared to wear a robe. Not the scarlet, but my Chambers black.'

Thus clad I confronted the controls. With the Superintendent's assistance I made one or two practice shunts, allowing my confidence to grow a little.

'Remember to watch the line ahead,' were his last words as he waved me off.

'Roger and out,' I replied.

Josefa proved an enthusiastic worker with the shovel. For the first half mile all went well. Looking back I noticed that, unlike Uncle Martin, I at least had acquired passengers. A gang of cutters had jumped aboard the waggons. They were swinging their legs over the sides and singing loudly. In the fields friends and relatives waved encouragement. As I manoeuvred the engine along the bends in the narrow-gauge track, my iron steed took on a rollicking and galloping motion. A sudden picture of the famous Mr Justice Powell flashed through my mind. This indomitable personage had been hurrying on his way to the Bodmin Assize in 1726 when his coachman was taken ill with the palsy. Six hours later the coach came rattling into the town in the teeth of a snowstorm with the judge himself at the reins. It was something I must remember to tell Mr Sharma.

'What's that, lordship?' Josefa inquired behind me, hearing my chuckle.

The Train of Progress

I was halfway through telling him the story when a loud screeching interrupted me. Forgetting to keep our eyes on the pressure-dial for a few minutes, we had allowed too great a build-up of steam. The result was the setting-off of an alarm hooter which was now firmly stuck. With one accord my passengers had flung themselves off into the undergrowth. It was hardly surprising that children, standing alongside the track, ran screaming to their mothers. The sight of a black-gowned figure, white face flecked with streaks of soot, caused immense alarm. Leaning out, I saw for myself the effect on the crossing-gate keeper, at the entrance to Lodoni village. Instead of throwing open the wooden barrier the man stood there mesmerized. Desperately, I applied the brakes. There was a jolt as the engine hit the five-bar slats and left the track. I found myself grinding to a halt dangerously close to the Official Reception Committee, gathered on the steps of the tiny new court-house thirty feet away. Always cool, Mr Sharma moved briskly across to an ancient horn gramophone draped with the Union Jack.

As I stepped down from the cab the National Anthem petered out in a funereal groan.

'Lodoni welcomes the Honourable Judge,' called Mr Sharma, 'His lordship will now proceed to cut the ribbon.'

Inspection revealed that the Registrar's immense length of red tape had become inextricably entangled in the front bogies of the engine.

'Thank you, Mr Sharma,' I replied. 'I think we can safely say that the ribbon is already severed.'

From my point of view, the rest of the proceedings went by in a kind of haze. I remember being seated upon a wide ceremonial mat as I was plied with ceremonial bowls of kava before a large crowd. After this a male-voice choir broke into song and a display of indigenous dancing took place. Then came the Grand Finale. A conga-like procession wended in and out of the trees to the accompaniment of loud shrieks and whistles.

'They have devised a brand new *meke*,' Chief Epeli explained. 'In words and movement they are depicting how your lordship arrived in Lodoni on this memorable day.'

Leading the conga was a rather sinister figure. His face was daubed with white powder and he was wearing a missionary's old black frock-coat.

'And the person in front?' I enquired.

The Chief smiled.

'He is our village jester, representing His Honour the Judge. Like your lordship, he makes the people laugh!'

It was an immensely popular performance. The singing and chanting went on for some hours. At the end, by general acclaim, there was an encore of the *meke*. Pleading a headache I retreated to the Rest House for sleep. On the following morning horses were provided for our return journey.

Back at work in the capital, it was hard to believe that this adventure had ever taken place. I pushed the whole thing to the back of my mind – like many another episode in my chequered judicial career. Until the following Monday morning.

I happened to be sitting in court for a plea in mitigation by Emu Buksh, now doyen of the local Bar. He was defending the Verger who had stolen the Sunday collection at the Wesleyan Church.

'My client is of blameless character and deeply regrets his folly. But suddenly. How shall I say?'

Mr Buksh raised his hands for dramatic effect.

'He went off the rails!'

There was a pause.

'Your lordship is familiar with the expression?'

'I am, Mr Buksh,' I replied.

Just then, I caught an unfamiliar sound from the Registrar's desk below the Bench.

Mr Sharma was laughing.

Chapter Fifteen

On the Rocks

O N THE FACE OF IT, my Chief Justice had every
right to demand an explanation from me.

'It's bad enough to have you, the divorce judge,
caught up in a domestic triangle,' he stormed. 'What
makes your conduct unpardonable is your personal in-
volvement in the very matrimonial dispute you were
sent to try!'

'I had to sleep somewhere, sir.'

'But not in the same room as the respondent's wife,
for heaven's sake!'

'I don't think you quite understand the problem, sir.'

'And what problem might that be?' Sir Neville
demanded icily.

'Naisomosomo is the smallest atoll in the Taula
chain,' I began. 'Accommodation is extremely limited.'

There was a choking sound from the other end of the
line, then silence. 'Hello sir . . . hello . . . operator . . .'

Sir Neville had replaced the receiver. This was a pity,
the points I was trying to get across being vital. The
parties in the case were Mr and Mrs Whippy, the sole
inhabitants of Naisomosomo where they kept the lighthouse. Because of what the local Matrimonial Causes
Ordinance termed 'unhappy conjugal differences', Mr
Whippy wanted a separation from his wife. I had been

sent on the Supreme Court launch to adjudicate in the matter.

'I'm not trying to pass the buck, sir,' I told Sir Neville when, sometime later, I had succeeded in getting through to him again. What with the ancient wind-up telephone and the inquisitive habits of Lola, the exchange operator down at the village, this was never an easy task. 'Had Mr Registrar Sharma been a little more flexible over our timetable, sir, the situation need never have arisen.'

'How on earth has the Registrar got anything to do with it?'

'Well, Mr Sharma insisted upon taking the launch on to Sivatoka to collect an outstanding fine.'

'So?'

'As I told him, sir – "There's no urgency, Mr Sharma, about collecting two shillings for keeping an unlicensed pig!"'

I took a deep breath and plunged on.

'I asked Mr Sharma to hang on so that we could deal with the case of Whippy *v.* Whippy first.'

'What difference would that have made?'

'Well, sir, I was to use the launch for the court hearing the next day, in any event. Had Mr Sharma agreed to wait I would have slept as usual in the cabin.'

Sir Neville sighed.

'I've already spoken to the Registrar about the incident,' he said.

So now the cat was out of the bag, I thought. Pretty underhand of Mr Sharma, all things considered, especially in view of my promise to recommend him for an increment in his salary.

'He tried to defend you, of course,' Sir Neville continued.

'Ah.'

A Case of Bananas

'But it's all too obvious that you showed your customary indecision.'

That was a distinctly unfair jibe on the part of the Chief Justice. After all, it had been precisely when Mr Sharma and I were actually discussing *what to do* that the offer of hospitality had arrived – via Mr Whippy himself!

'I wasn't in any sense sharing the part of the lighthouse occupied by Mr and Mrs Whippy, Sir Neville.'

'Then how on earth did you come to be locked in a room with the lady for most of the night?'

'It was not me who locked the door, sir. It was Mrs Whippy and she then concealed the key, er, about her person.'

'A pretty compromising situation, would you not agree, Knox Mawer?'

'Mr Whippy is a man of ungovernable temper, sir.'

I could hear my Chief clicking his false teeth irascibly.

'I gather from the Registrar that Mr Whippy's suspicions were first aroused by your conduct in the swimming pool.'

'It was just that the diving board gave way, sir. Put up during the war, sir, by the American army.'

'Spare me the US Cavalry in this sordid Wild West saga!' snapped Sir Neville. His tone was distinctly unamused. 'Can't take any more of this telephone conversation,' he announced.

The crackling on the line was increasing and Lola's heavy breathing had intensified as she listened spellbound at the switchboard.

'Security's nothing like it should be,' he said.

I could hear him rustling away the file.

'For God's sake, man, get the whole thing down on paper,' he concluded. 'I shall expect your report next week, at the latest!'

On the Rocks

Setting everything out in black and white was a near-impossible task. How was I to describe Mr and Mrs Whippy for a start? Hardly ordinary characters, even by island standards!

Mrs W was certainly no lotus-flower. Of Amazonian build she claimed, amongst her ancestors, the warrior Queen Taloma of Guadpia. Taloma had throttled with her bare hands the notorious Bully Staines, the most feared pirate in the South Seas. As for Mr W, he had an Irish father, hence perhaps the wild mane of red hair and pugilistic disposition. His Maori mother had given him a swarthy complexion and the muscles of a weight-lifter. All in all, the two of them were an even match. This they proved on the morning after my night at the lighthouse when Mr W's grip on his wife's scruff had been countered by her sharp teeth in his arm. The case-papers before me had been sent flying until the contestants were separated by Mr Sharma's threat of summary judgment for contempt of court. However, I was getting events in the wrong order. My report began –

Firstly, about the Incident in the Swimming-pool, sir. Mr Sharma had left in the launch. I was installed on a camp-bed on the topmost floor of the lighthouse, just below the beacon. Before retiring, I took a moonlight dip, little thinking that Mrs Whippy would take it into her head to do the same. I was resting on the diving board when it suddenly collapsed. The wood must have been rotten and I fell like a stone on top of Mrs Whippy.

I paused. The memory of it all had brought me out in a cold sweat. I dabbed at the smudge of ink with my blotting-pad.

Before I could free myself from the mix-up, Mr Whippy emerged from the doorway. He pulled his wife out and a fracas ensued. I thought it best to beat a retreat to my quarters. I had no wish to become a pawn in some matrimonial power-game, especially as I was to be trying the case the next day. However, soon afterwards, I heard the padding of feet of Mrs Whippy on the spiral staircase. She burst into my little sanctuary and locked the door behind in a state of some distress. She told me that Mr Whippy was 'after me with a carving knife'. I decided not to risk confirming this allegation. Besides, there was another crisis on hand.

I leaned back and rang the bell for a large whisky and soda to spur me on to the completion of my written explanation.

In his fury, Mr Whippy had knocked out the generator which was alongside the pool. Hence the beacon had gone out. At the same time as Mrs W had come into my room, an emergency call rang out from the phone on the wall. From the other end I heard the rasping tones of the New Zealand Marine Engineer in Auckland. He demanded to know what the blank blank was going on. Local shipping had reported the lighthouse out of action and, whoever I was, would I get the blank thing working again!

It was really making quite an exciting story, I thought, on reading back so far.

My knowledge of diesel machinery, Sir Neville, is extremely limited. But I did not wish to have a shipwreck on my conscience, in addition to everything else. So with Mrs Whippy's help I managed to find some kerosene and light the wick of the original Victorian paraffin warning-lamp. It seemed almost nightmarish, crouching there under the dome, by the flickering shadow of a great flame, high above the rocks of this solitary outpost.

On the Rocks

I paused. Was I making the report too colourful for my Chief Justice? No. I wanted him fully to realize the strange pressures of my predicament. I continued –

There was no sound from below. Mr Whippy had passed out in an alcoholic stupor, no doubt. Mrs Whippy, nevertheless, seemed reluctant to leave the safety of my room. Fortunately, the ship's cook had given me a thermos flask and cold supper to take ashore. Together we shared a cup of hot Bovril and a ham sandwich. At this point, Mrs Whippy started to confide certain of her matrimonial difficulties. Naturally, I had to warn her that this was strictly *sub judice*. I brought out my travelling-rug and hung it between us, for the sake of *due propriety*. We both retired to sleep. The next morning I was awoken by the hooter of the launch which had returned with Mr Sharma to the lagoon. Back on board I informed the Registrar of what had transpired. The parties were summoned to open court. Or, rather, open deck, I should say. Another tussle took place as afore-mentioned. I informed them that the court proposed to adjourn, so that a judge less acquainted with the parties – yourself Sir Neville – could adjudicate in the matter.

With a sigh of relief, I folded up my missive and dis-patched it with Josefa to catch the next mail. It would be some months before I heard back, I assumed.

Yet less than a week later, my telephone rang. It was Sir Neville, but his tone was now altogether different.

'This business of your stepping into the breach and lighting the lamp?' he said. 'Why on earth didn't you tell me in the first place? No sense in hiding one's light under a bushel.'

'Well, sir,' I began.

'Anyway,' he interrupted, 'I'm informed by His Excellency the Governor that you are to receive an Official Commendation for Resourcefulness in an Emergency from the Antipodean Lifeboat Association.'

I gulped.

'That certainly adds credit to my Judicial Department. Albeit, in rather unusual circumstances.'

'What about Mr and Mrs Whippy, sir?'

'The case will be filed away under the heading UN-RESOLVED.'

Sir Neville produced one of his rare witticisms.

'Perhaps we should call it a local version of the Bermuda Triangle!'

Perhaps we should.

Chapter Sixteen

A Case of Censorship

'WHY NOT POP OVER to me for tiffin?' read the note from J.S. It was a cheering thought as my morning session in Nasoro court had not exactly gone with a swing.

For a start there was the hiatus over the court exhibit box. The all-important key to the box was kept by Josefa on a piece of string around his neck. Unfortunately, while swimming under water in the lagoon in search of his favourite breakfast of baby octopus, the string had been snapped by an inquisitive tentacle. Over an hour was wasted combing the coral reef without success. The guilty octopus, too, had gone into hiding.

'I shall have to dismiss all the cases of tax evasion,' I told him. 'As we're no longer able to get at the documentary proof. Unless your eight-legged friend decides to return his stolen property,' I added, always game for a laugh. For once Josefa looked glum. After all, he had also lost his breakfast!

Next, a prosecution of grievous bodily harm ended in confusion when it was revealed that the complainant's injury was self-inflicted. The foolish fellow had apparently run his head against a coconut tree, hoping to make it look like an assault by the village-crier who had absconded with his wife. I suggested that he report it to

the Marriage Guidance Council, a one-woman organiz-
ation in the shape of the redoubtable Mattie Mafua who
was proving quite a success on the island.

Finally, I had to deal with a complaint by Chang Yee,
the local store-keeper. He was claiming damages for the
loss of two packets of Scotts Porridge Oats. It seemed
they had been enjoyed by a hungry goat belonging to the
Methodist Mission. After some thought, I awarded the
goat to Mr Yee by way of compensation. It seemed a
sensible enough judgment, until the goat decided to join
in the argument by dealing me a painful butt in the
groin as I was supervising the enforcement of the
decree.

All in all, I was looking forward to the lunchtime
break although, as it turned out, J.S. did nothing to
cheer me up.

'Might as well face it, old chap,' he said, settling back
into his long cane-chair with its frayed arms and creaking legs. 'We're a dying species.' He eyed me up and
down thoughtfully. 'Dead in your case I should say.'

There was no denying that the changeover to self-
government for the remaining Pacific Territories,
announced by Whitehall, did raise a question mark over
the future.

Repressing a bout of hiccups, J.S. stood up, whisky
glass in hand, and moved across the verandah to the
piano.

'Help yourself to another corned-beef fritter.'

'I've done very well, thank you,' I said.

J.S.'s fritters were always grilled by his olf cook to
wrought-iron consistency, and one had to bear in mind
that Mr W.R. Lal, the nearest dentist, was over on
Malaika, two hundred miles away.

'The Song is Ended but the Melody Lingers on,' J.S.
sang loudly, accompanied by a discordant series of

chords in the wrong key.

'You could call it our theme tune,' he said, as he launched into *Just a Song at Twilight*.

After three or four reprises he closed the piano lid and refreshed his glass. 'Of course,' he added, 'now that HMG is replacing career officers with contract men we're bound to have some fairly unsuitable characters arriving on the scene. Have you come across this Inspector McVie yet?'

As a matter of fact I had.

'Started off life as a dog-handler with the Glasgow Police, believe it or not,' said J.S. 'Fellow never gives up when he's after his quarry. Just like his damned Alsatians.'

Angus McVie had not been long in the South Pacific. His close-cropped ginger head and handle-bar moustache put me in mind of another Scot, my regimental sergeant-major with the Sixth Royal Horse Artillery in the Second World War. 'Get your hair cut or we'll have to buy you a bleeding violin,' was what I expected McVie to bellow at me when we first met. In fact, his initial greeting had been just as memorable when he first presented himself in my Circuit Chambers.

'Request warrant to arrest the jailer Tomasi Bikilevu,' the Inspector had barked.

'The jailer?' I repeated in astonishment. 'For what offence, in heaven's name?'

'Aiding and abetting a convict to escape.'

'How on earth?'

'Apprehended on Christmas Day.'

'But in what circumstances?'

McVie took a deep breath, still standing rigidly to attention.

'Having kept watch upon the said jailer's quarters for

three hours twenty five minutes from a position of cover in the breadfruit tree outside, I burst in upon the suspect. I caught the villain in the very act.'

'What act?'

'Sitting down to Christmas dinner with a convict, one Semi Isikeli by name. Said to be a cousin of the said jailer.'

'The jailer's quarters are inside the prison, are they not, Inspector?'

'Correct.'

'Well, the convict hadn't exactly escaped from the prison, had he?'

'Have to report he was not wearing the Correct Apparel with Regulation Arrows.'

'What was he wearing?'

'Balu-shirt, beach shorts and a lei of holly and hibiscus. Highly irregular.'

I shook my head.

'A spot of over-indulgence on the jailer's part, part of the Yuletide spirit, Inspector. Nothing more serious than that, I'm afraid. After all, Christmas is a family affair. I suggest you drop the investigation with an admonishment.'

Inspector McVie did not take kindly to my decision.

But J.S. nodded approvingly as I related the incident.

'One has to be flexible in these far-flung places, after all,' he said. 'Use one's imagination a bit. Perhaps you remember that case of mine in Vatua?'

I certainly did.

There had been some trouble over the custody of a newly born Vatuan child. Two fathers claimed paternity and, despite the mother's efforts at peace-making, they had come to blows about it. J.S. was sitting as magistrate and had finally lost patience. He had what he described as a brainwave.

'Following the Bible we shall make a "judgment of Solomon",' he told them. 'If you can't agree, the boy will have to be cut in two, and a half given to each of you. Fair enough?'

The uproar that followed this pronouncement could be heard several villages away. But at least it put a decisive end to the wrangle.

'Made 'em come to their senses, d'y' see,' J.S. told me with satisfaction. 'Recommend it to you should you come up against the same kind of case. In the end, they settled on the boy spending six months alternatively with each claimant as I'd originally suggested. Suited the lad, himself, to the ground. So delighted he still keeps hanging around my place. Running errands for me and so on.

'They christened him after me, too,' he added, 'which means a regular order for Harrogate Toffee from the Army and Navy Stores on my account.'

The trouble with J.S. was that he sometimes allowed a taste for the bizarre to run away with him. There was the matter of the Barbara Cartland novels, for instance.

J.S. had strong literary enthusiasms of his own, being devoted to Henty, Marryat, Conan Doyle and John Buchan. When a gift of books to the island hospital arrived one day from the Red Cross he had eagerly supervised the opening of the consignment. To his horror, the parcel contained over 100 novels by the veteran mistress of romantic fiction.

'Have to stop this Western trash polluting the ethnic customs of Melanesia,' he declared.

Unfortunately, in a dog-eared copy of the *Illustrated London News*, he had recently come upon an article by Arthur Bryant which described the method used by the sixteenth-century courts in dealing with heretical writing. Thus inspired, J.S. had promptly ordered a large bonfire to be made in the office compound.

'In my capacity as Justice of the Peace I condemn these books to be burnt by the Common Hangman,' he decreed. Apart from the fact that there was no such personage as a Common Hangman J.S. was, of course, without any authority whatsoever to order the destruction of this charitable donation.

'Never seem to get any credit for a show of spirit,' he complained, when the inevitable reprimand arrived from his superiors.

J.S. puffed defiantly upon an immense cheroot.

As usual, in times of trouble, he had seated himself at the piano. From a broken-down Gladstone bag he had unearthed a treasure of sheet-music from the twenties and thirties, a birthday present from his elder sister. Pages kept falling to pieces but he managed quite well.

Finally, he peered round at me in the flickering light of his extremely old pressure-lamp.

'Which brings me back to my original question. As a dying species, what does the future hold for us? Can't see us as "contract men", can you?'

He downed another large swig.

'We'd better make plans.'

Chapter Seventeen

Constitutional Casualty

'A H. Come in, Knox Mawer,' called Sir Neville
Gawsby.

The Chief Justice's well-appointed chambers commanded a splendid view of Suba Bay. The air-
conditioning system purred gently. On a sidetable stood
a silver coffee-pot, alongside a half-empty cup. A second
cup was not in evidence.

'Do sit down,' said my CJ, indicating a hard-backed
chair constructed with the usual genius for discomfort
shown by Her Majesty's Public Works Department.
Even as he spoke, Sir Neville edged his own padded
leather seat to a safe distance away from me. Ever since
I had sat alongside him on the Bench in the Tailevu
Bumboat Appeal he had regarded me as a dangerous
source of contagion. I was suffering from my familiar
upper-respiratory infection at the time and had been
unable to control a prolonged bout of sneezing during
Sir Neville's delivery of judgment. The cold he caught
was 'the worst I've ever had in my life', he told me later.
Took a double course of antibiotics to have any effect.'

All that was very much in the past, and the CJ's
present concern was 'to discuss my future' as he put it.

'As you know,' he began, 'the Suba Independence Bill
is going through Parliament at this very moment. In

addition, the Protection Treaty between Tofua and the UK has not been renewed, leaving them to manage their own affairs from now onwards.'

'The wind of change, sir,' I observed knowledgeably.

Sir Neville stood up and strode across to a large globe standing on a pedestal in the bay-window. He was dressed in immaculately creased blue shorts ready for his afternoon golf. Those muscular legs, I thought enviously, they seemed to have been custom-built for judicial knee-breeches. Beckoning for me to join him he gave the world a spin so that the large blue segment of the South Pacific was on the top. I peered down at the sprinkling of tiny dots.

'At least I'll still be left with the Shebas,' I said.

'Their date for autonomy has already been fixed. Similarly with the Vellice Isles.'

'What about the Sullivans?'

'To become the Republic of Muvalu, I understand.'

I moved my finger nine hundred nautical miles eastwards.

'How about the Sullivan Group?' I asked.

'To become yet another Republic, I'm afraid. Viribiti will be its name.'

In some despair I took a stab at the New Orkneys – a chain of fever-ridden swamps.

'Scheduled for total self-government at about the same time,' declared the CJ.

With a dying fall the globe creaked to a standstill. Purposefully, Sir Neville returned to his desk. Alongside his set of *All England Law Reports (1897 et seq.)* I noticed a stack of brochures advertising property for sale in the Mediterranean.

'I suppose I'm fortunate,' he said. 'A full retirement pension is infinitely more profitable than the golden handshake. So we'll be looking for a sunny spot by the sea for my yacht, with plenty of snorkelling and a good local wine.'

'So where does all this leave me, sir?' I asked after a moment or two. Sir Neville rubbed his jaw thoughtfully.

'Ah. Yes.'

From under his copy of the *Financial Times* he fished out a buff file marked OHMS.

'All explained in here,' he said. 'You're to have six weeks paid leave and then report to Whitehall for further directions.'

He cleared his throat.

'Meanwhile, there's a favour I want you to do for me.'

Sir Neville pulled open the bottom drawer of his desk and took out a large rexine case marked Charmcraft, Hatton Gardens.

'Every serving magistrate in my Department is to receive one of these commemorative medals.'

'Very nice, sir,' I murmured, examining the specimen that he had handed to me. It was slightly smaller than a Rotary Club badge and of considerably cheaper quality.

'My own brainchild,' said the CJ. 'Intend to award them at an official reception here on Maundy Thursday.'

'What exactly is depicted here, sir?' I asked.

'Silver scales of justice, of course,' he replied, snatching it back. 'Emblazoned on a royal blue background.'

The Chief Justice popped the midget token into an envelope. 'Coming to the point,' he went on, 'I believe J.S. Pennington is a friend of yours?'

I nodded cautiously.

'Pennington's already informed my secretary that he won't be attending the presentation ceremony. Says he's got a full diary. Feeble excuse. But seeing that he's the longest serving JP in the whole of the South Pacific, I can hardly pass him over.'

I maintained a tactful silence.

'Since you'll be in his neck of the woods on your final circuit I want you to take Pennington's award along for him.'

'Certainly, Sir Neville,' I said.

I paused to pick up the file concerning my future.

'Just one thing, CJ,' I said. 'These further directions from HMG – have you any idea where they might be leading?'

For the first time ever, the Chief Justice laid a hand on my shoulder. 'Don't worry. Whitehall has everything in hand. They've even given you your own special category,' he said, 'you'll see.'

The door was closed firmly behind me.

Outside, I put on my reading glasses. There it was on the label, clear to see. KNOX MAWER. R. And in red ink brackets alongside, the words CONSTITUTIONAL CASUALTY.

'Constitutional Casualty!'

J.S. rolled the phrase around, before washing it down with a double tot of Black Label.

'At least they're packing you back to Blighty as Walking Wounded. Best I can hope for seems to be a free funeral!'

We were leaning over the rail of his verandah as the sun went down over the thatched huts of the village and the lagoon beyond.

'With all your years of service, J.S.,' I said, 'you're bound to be left comfortably off.'

'Not a bit of it, old boy.'

He fished a crumpled paper from the pocket of his bush-jacket. It was a letter from the Government Secretariat, scattered with explosive underlinings and exclamation marks in J.S.'s indelible pencil. I studied it carefully.

'Did you really lose two Government Launches through negligence?'

'Afraid so.'

'Two!'

'The reef around Naisatu is notorious,' he replied loftily. 'A hazard of nature was the way I expressed it. But *they* took no notice, naturally.'

I read on. The list of monies set off against J.S.'s pension seemed endless.

'Have you never paid the rent due for your official quarters?'

He thought hard for a moment.

'I settled up in 1937, I seem to remember. But I was a new boy, then, of course.'

The letter ended with an enormous demand for income tax arrears.

'Leaves me with a pittance, as you see. Certainly not enough to retire on.' He lit up an evil-smelling cheroot and was enveloped in a cloud of yellow smoke.

'So what are your plans?' I enquired.

He tapped his head mysteriously.

'All in the old brain cells here. Tell you later.'

'That reminds me,' I said. I brought out the medallion from Sir Neville.

'Allow me, District Commissioner.' I was about to pin it to his lapel, but J.S. took it from me.

'Been having trouble with these braces for days.'

I had to admit that the CJ's Award made an ideal replacement for a missing trouser button.

'Very useful,' approved J.S. happily. 'Please thank Sir Neville on my behalf.'

Throwing himself down into his wicker chair he turned his attention to the airmail copy of *The Times* he'd been using as a fly-swat.

A Case of Bananas

'Some people get their awards from a bit higher up, of course.' Shaking his head he was perusing the Queen's Birthday Honours List. 'I see she's given a decoration to Bubbles Berkley,' he muttered.

'Can't say I know the name,' I said.

'No reason why you should. Anyway, Bubbles has been made a Knight Commander of the Order of St George. Bloody fool. Couldn't even command a camel when we were political officers together in the Hadramaut.'

I took the vacant chair alongside him and asked for some more tonic water in my gin. At this point a cacophony of excited shouts and cries disturbed the calm of dusk. J.S. suddenly threw down the newspaper and dashed from the verandah in the direction of the servants' command.

'Sorry about that,' he said, upon his return. 'Little Toto, the cook's five-year-old, was about to decapitate his sister with my ceremonial sword. My fault entirely. They've been having a great time going through my cabin-trunk. I certainly won't be needing my Colonial Service uniform, wherever I go.'

Even as he spoke, a sound like an out-of-tune bugle drifted across from the village.

'That hunting horn of mine seems to be amusing them, too.'

He sighed.

'Used to lead the Pennington Beagle Pack with that, going after jackals in the desert.'

With a reminiscent smile, J.S. resumed his perusal of the Honours List. 'My God! Postleton Jones has got a CMG.'

'Has he, indeed,' I said, trying to sound interested.

'Meaning "Call me God" in his case, of course. No doubt he has hopes for a GCMG, eventually – "God calls me God".' J.S. emitted one of those loud barks that signified a joke. This was followed by a cry of rage as he bent over the small print at the bottom of the List.

'Not a VSM for that villain Babu Handa?'

He chomped down a fistful of cashew nuts.

'It's an insult to the dog,' he declared.

'Dog?'

'Surely you remember. They gave the Victoria Service Medal to Laddie, that splendid St Bernard with the box round his neck who used to be on duty at Waterloo Station collecting money for the blind.'

'And what did Mr Handa do?'

'He didn't exactly have a box round his neck. But he was just as good at collecting money. He was my clerk until he got promoted to Establishment Officer Grade 3.'

He clicked his tongue.

'They told me afterwards he was charging 5 rupees entrance fee just to line up outside my office for an interview.'

With a rattle he turned back over the page to where the new peerages were announced.

'I see Sir Henry Colston's been made a baron,' he commented. 'Served under him as a cadet. Ah. The days of youth!'

He trumpeted loudly into his handkerchief, always a sign of strong emotion. 'Taken the title Lord Mata-Mata. Comes from New Zealand, d'you see. Not his fault.'

J.S. refilled his glass.

'Wouldn't mind a title myself. Lord Savage, say.'

I looked puzzled.

'The Savage Islands,' he exclaimed. 'My last posting.'

'What about Baron Christmas?' I suggested.

J.S. had once served on Christmas Island before it was taken over by the military.

'Might get mistaken for Santa Claus,' was J.S.'s reply.

A Case of Bananas

'All the same,' he pondered, 'Mother would have liked a title for me. Always keen on Honours and all that.'

J.S.'s mother, a sprightly ninety-year-old, lived in a nursing home in Leamington Spa where she ruled the nurses with a rod of iron while keeping them informed of the careers of her numerous sons – all serving the Crown in various ways, Major-General, Rear-Admiral, Air Vice-Marshal, Ambassador, and so on. There were daughters, too, married with children. All seemed happy to keep their connection with J.S. at a distance, I had observed.

'Mother had an annual order with the stork,' J.S. informed me. 'I was the last and a bit of a let-down, from all accounts. Everyone said she should have sent me back and kept the stork. He seemed to be an efficient creature, at least.'

Apparently, J.S.'s mother had a soft spot for the youngest of the family.

'Her age makes her a bit absent-minded,' said J.S. 'I mean, she still sends my prep-school allowance every week – a ten shilling postal order for tuck addressed to Master Johnnie Pennington.'

He jerked his head in the direction of the stack of packing cases from the Liquor Department of the Army and Navy Stores.

'Pays for the corkage on that stuff, anyway. Very decent of Ma. Mean to pop over to Leamington and see her, whenever I get a little spare time.'

Just then Batu, the cook, came in to say we should be eating in ten minutes time. Batu was wearing one of J.S.'s old topees, I noticed.

'You know where to wash your hands, old boy,' said J.S. It was his usual euphemism for the thunderbox W.C. shrouded in Samoan ivy at the back of the house.

Constitutional Casualty

'Curry,' enthused J.S. when I rejoined him. 'Freshly caught saluka.' Before I could stop him J.S. ladled out and placed before me the head and shoulders of an enormous fish.

'I'd prefer you to have the eyes,' I demurred, making some swift rearrangement on my plate.

J.S. ate at enormous speed. As he helped himself to another mound of mashed breadfruit he cast me a fierce glare.

'How long are you going to push that food around?' he demanded. 'Essential to try to build yourself up. Part of your convalescence now you're a Constitutional Casualty!'

A barrage of similar jokes involving crutches, bandages and invalid chairs was kept up by J.S. for the rest of the meal.

'So what do you plan to do with your life?' I countered, when we had exhausted this vein of humour and were taking coffee back on the verandah. 'Turn beachcomber perhaps?'

He drew himself up with dignity.

'I shall be commuting,' he replied.

'From Leamington?'

'Do be serious! Between the islands, is what I mean.'

'Doing what?'

'Consultancy,' he announced, obviously a word he had picked up from the appointments section of *The Times*. 'I'll have my base at the United Services Club in Suba. Only problem is that I shall have to book two separate apartments in the Annexe. Can't stand the sound of anybody snoring.'

Having frequently stayed with J.S. and suffered the gruesome sound-effects coming from the Commissioner's bedroom during his hours of slumber, I felt his fellow residents at the Club would welcome this arrangement.

'Then, from the Club, I'll be taking off in my dinghy at regular intervals.'

'In any particular direction?'

'To Numea for a start. As you discovered for yourself, the folks there seem rather keen to have me stick around.'

'Doing what exactly?'

'With self-government there's bound to be more red tape than ever. People will be needing a spot of disinterested advice as to how to deal with officialdom.'

'Will you be part of HMG's Overseas Aid Programme then?'

'Certainly not,' he replied indignantly. 'I'm going independent like everybody else.'

'So you'll move all over the South Pacific?'

'That's right. A kind of floating Citizens Advice Bureau.'

J.S. began to wind up his Mickey Mouse alarm clock.

'Time to turn in,' he declared.

By my bed J.S. had placed a bizarre collection of reading matter – *Oceanic Languages* published by the Auckland Theological Press, the *Guinness Book of Records*, *Among the Basutus: A Grim Story* by Mrs J. Nettleton, and a translation from the German of a work by Dr Ernst Schacht, entitled *British Imperialism* (University of Heidelberg, 1909).

'The marked insularity of character to which, by geographical accident, the English are doomed, is made worse by prolonged residence in tropical outposts,' Dr Schacht observed in the Preface. 'They become a species whose peculiar behaviour can only be regarded with bewilderment.' I fell asleep with these observations racing through my mind.

Next morning the cook served me a breakfast of paw-paw and porridge, alone on the rear verandah. When J.S. appeared he was wearing a striking tarpa robe of native bark-cloth. He popped the spear he was carrying into the umbrella stand and joined me at the table.

'Looks as though you should have a pleasant trip,' he said, pointing in the direction of the reef. 'Water's as smooth as a lake.'

I nodded, still transfixed by his appearance. The strong fishy smell that now pervaded the breakfast table was obviously some kind of tribal body-lotion.

'Don't you find the, er . . . outfit rather hot and sticky at this time of year?' I ventured.

J.S. glanced down at himself.

'Have to make a speech at a farewell gathering of the Toloans this afternoon. Since they were kind enough to make me their Honorary Chief, the least I can do is to dress and anoint myself correctly.'

Breakfast over, Josefa arrived at the wheel of the Island Tricycle Taxi. He quickly stowed my luggage on the roof-rack. I was about to make my farewells to J.S. but, for the moment, his attention was elsewhere.

'Batu,' he yelled in the direction of the cook's quarters. 'Those wretched tomb bats are roosting up in the banyan tree again. Bring me the scatter-gun at once.'

A shower of cartridge pellets fell on our taxi as we moved away. Once again the words of Dr Schacht seemed strangely appropriate.

My last sight of J.S. was of a mighty figure waving to me from the verandah steps, the native spear in one hand, the scatter-gun in the other.

'I'll give you a ring from Leamington Spa,' he called as we turned in the direction of the wharf.

Chapter Eighteen

The Retreading Process

I WAS to be retreaded. This sinister word had been coined in the corridors of power for a surplus minion of the Crown like me. With the end of Empire I had to be pressed into some fresh kind of service. The expression made me feel distinctly uneasy. An image of Charlie Chaplin sprang to mind, caught up in the fiendish machinery of *Modern Times*. Was I to be strapped upon a kind of bureaucratic conveyor-belt, dropped into some huge melting-pot and churned out as a civil-servant clone with all traces of my former existence erased for ever?

'How exactly would it be done in my case, Sir George?' I asked. My retirement leave had ended and I was being interviewed by the top legal mandarin in Whitehall, Sir George Hardcastle QC.

'Well, for a start,' he replied, gazing at me sternly over his half-moon spectacles, 'we'll need to have you thoroughly reoriented.'

'Reoriented, sir?'

'Indeed. Get you accustomed to present-day practice in the courts of the United Kingdom. We want you back at the Bar for a start.'

I was retreating through the outer office when the lock on my new briefcase (made in Taiwan) suddenly gave

The Retreading Process

way. It was a bit over-full because I had squeezed in a packet of corned-beef sandwiches for an economy lunch. As I stopped to retrieve my inoculation papers, under the weary gaze of a teenage secretary, I overheard Sir George on the phone.

'Yes,' he was saying, 'I've just had a word with Knox Mawer. He's been laying down the law in some tinpot Pacific island for the last twenty years. Heaven knows whether we'll ever be able to fit him in.'

I rather gained the impression that Sir George was anxious to get me out of his hair. He certainly made sure that I was stationed as far as possible from his London office. A spell on the Northern Circuit was to be my sentence.

I was told to apply to Oriel Chambers, Liverpool, a gloomy Victorian edifice in Water Street overlooking a windswept landing-stage and rundown warehouse. The list of barristers' names inscribed in gothic lettering in the hallway was impressive – at least to a newcomer like myself – Ramsbottom, Outhwaite, Saddleby, Wrigglesworth.

'Naturally, they're all out in court,' explained Mr Arthur Briggs, introducing himself. 'We're a pretty successful team here.' Mr Briggs modestly called himself the Chief Clerk but, within minutes, it was obvious that his true role was one of puppet-master. In between arranging court appearances and solicitors' conferences, I could see him sizing me up. There was only a single vacancy. Could I be profitably jerked into action at the end of the spare string? It was made politely clear that, should I not suit, other puppets were available, stocked up in the wings.

What decided the issue was my success with the milk carton. Mr Briggs confided that he had a duodenal ulcer. This required a liquid refreshment at intervals of thirty minutes. Alongside his desk, upon a side-table, stood a freshly made pot of tea and an unopened carton of Express Dairy Milk. In the middle of our discussion Mr Briggs was called to the phone again. I saw him eye the empty cup. Perhaps I could help.

I put on my spectacles. 'To open push back wings to full extent then draw forward to form a spout' it said on the carton. For once, I managed to follow instructions without disaster.

'Well done,' approved Mr Briggs. 'The gentleman I was interviewing earlier this morning made a right mess of it. All over my trousers.'

He glanced down at the still-damp patch on his thigh, taking a grateful gulp of his tea.

There was a silence.

Finally, he held out his hand.

'I hope you'll be very happy with us,' he said.

That same afternoon I was assigned a desk in the shadowy back corner of Oriel Chambers. As I pulled up my chair I found myself seated alongside the glass partition of the Chief Clerk's office. This meant that I was privy to what was going on in there – in detail.

His busiest time was 5 p.m. when the courts had adjourned. The light over his desk was flicked on and both telephones rang out simultaneously. Booking hour had begun. It heralded the sixty minutes when Mr Briggs hired out his barristers for future appearances.

Cast in my usual role of eavesdropper, it was apparent that he was doing his best for me with clients at the other end of the phone.

'Rather an unusual addition to our team,' was his usual way of mentioning me. 'Mature, of course. Even had experience on the Bench.'

There would be a pause.

'Yes. You could say he's been in practice down south.

If you mean the South Pacific, that is.'

Almost immediately I would hear the phone being replaced.

'Still no takers, I'm afraid,' I heard him confide to Joyce, the typist.

Fortunately, the rattle of Joyce's typewriter drowned out any further comments on my progress. At this point I would put aside the rest of the current *Law Reports* which I had spent the day mugging up and wander into the next room for a chat with the younger members of Chambers – Stanbridge, Boyston and Grimshaw.

At least it was flattering, I thought, the way the youngsters had taken to calling me CJ. Obviously, my former title as Chief Justice of the Vatua Levu Islands had impressed them.

The penny only dropped when Grimshaw clapped me on the shoulder as we were putting on our coats to leave.

'Well, Cannibal Jim,' he cried, 'how about standing us all a drink!'

'I expect he's got a bottle of rum in his locker,' quipped Stanbridge, who seemed to picture my former life as some sort of *Treasure Island* adventure.

But it was through Grimshaw's kindness that I got my first brief.

I happened to be sitting behind him in Court No. One at St George's Hall where he had a big case before the Recorder of Liverpool.

'Looks as though I shan't make Bootle tomorrow,' he said. 'Care to do the case for me?'

'Rather,' I said.

I hurried back in some triumph to Mr Briggs. As usual his left hand and ear were firmly attached to the telephone. With his other hand he passed me a dog-eared bundle of papers.

A Case of Bananas

'It's a Legal Aid Application for Bail,' he said. 'Bootle Magistrates Court. Conference 9.30 am sharp.'

The brief was to appear on behalf of Kevin McArtney, aged seventeen, charged with thirty-seven counts of car theft. My train departed from Liverpool Exchange, an ill-lit cavern scheduled for demolition.

'Half an hour to wait,' I was told.

At the entrance to the platform stood a crooked sign, 'Barber'.

The proprietor, a genial hunchback with yellow fangs, sat me in the chair.

'Any preference?' he asked.

'Just tidy it up,' I said as he began work. I was soon to know that my hairdresser's own previous experience was as an Army barber.

'Which regiment?' I asked him. 'Not the Royal Horse Artillery, my old outfit?'

'Military Prisons Division,' he grinned, removing the cigarette stump from his lip as a large fragment of ash fell on to my centre-parting. Even in a moment of relaxation I seemed unable to get away from the world of crime.

Certainly the work of the 'glasshouse' barber did not meet with the approval of my client, Kevin McArtney. A pimply youth, I found him sitting on the bench in the foyer of the Bootle court-house, combing his extensive locks. He greeted me with an offensive snigger. 'Looks as if you're the one who's been doing time,' he said. 'Talk about short back and sides!'

I ignored the jibe and tried to concentrate on the case papers. I had always had a special interest in the problems of teenage delinquency. Take the Samolan hill-tribes – to give but a single instance. During the 1959 Coconut Riots there, I had enacted a special Youth Custody scheme to deal with the teenage rebels who had

>elted the village elders with showers of half-ripe mis-
;iles after a night of kava drinking.

'Not much room for manoeuvre in your defence,
Kevin,' I said kindly. 'Can you explain how all these car
hefts began?'

'Nowt to explain,' he replied.

He turned out to be well versed in the law of crime,
having started at the age of nine.

'I'm pleading Not Guilty and Electing Trial,' he said,
removing a wodge of chewing-gum and sticking it under
he chair where my coat was folded. 'Got to get bail so
as not to miss the match.'

'So you're keen on football?'

He looked at me pityingly.

'I'm talking about afterwards,' he said. 'Man. United
fans versus the Everton Mob. Should be a good 'un.
Last time we won 9 to 5.'

'9 to 5?'

'Ambulance cases,' he explained briefly.

Fortunately, at that moment, the signal came for us to
move into court. Kevin's band of supporters followed
closely behind.

'May it please your worship,' I began.

I was addressing the formidable JP, Alderman Mrs
Gertrude Brandock. She was wearing a large black
toque better suited, I should have thought, for funerals.

'As you will see from the Probation Officer's report a
promise of a job has been obtained for my client.
Assuming you are disposed to release him upon bail,
ma'am.'

'I've no intention of doing that,' snapped Mrs
Braddock.

From my brief I produced a letter from a scrap-
merchant, the prospective employer.

'Surely the first step along the road to rehabilitation

in Kevin's case', I persisted, 'is steady employment, your worship.'

'The only steps this young man will be taking', said Mrs Braddock, 'are back to the Risley Remand Centre.'

I brought out a copy of the Bail Act. If this was to be a duel my own experience should have taught me a thing or two.

'I would request permission to draw your worship's attention to section 1B. If it pleases you, ma'am,' I repeated.

Mrs Brandock's face turned brick red. Her bosom was heaving.

'Nothing you are saying pleases me, Mr Knox Mawer.'

I took a deep breath.

'The Act requires that the court states its reason for refusing bail,' I persisted.

'The reason should be obvious. Even to you.'

I took a sip from a glass of dusty water in front of me and began to read the preamble to the Act.

'So far as the law is concerned, ma'am,' I said, 'may I emphasize that my client is innocent until proved guilty. He is entitled to his freedom as a right.'

'Right!' said Mrs Brandock scornfully. 'This young layabout doesn't begin to know what right is. You only have to look at his appalling record to know he's a menace to society.'

There was an indignant scuffling noise from behind me. The Bootle court arrangements meant that the public was crammed at close quarters to counsel's seat. Half-turning, I saw that I was hemmed in upon all sides by Kevin's family – his mother, various sisters and brothers, and a tiny, wizened old lady in a tartan shawl who was obviously his grandmother. Behind them was a row of schoolfriends, playing truant that day and furtively enjoying a large bag of oranges.

The Retreading Process

I turned my attention once more to the papers in front of me.

'Please allow me, ma'am, to develop my argument on the relevant law,' I said.

'Quite unnecessary,' Mrs Brandock rasped.

She drew her fur stole closer around her so that the snarling fox-head nestled under her chin.

It was at this point that I felt the blood surging up at the back of my neck. Who was this presumptuous amateur on the Bench, I asked myself? I could not escape the painful reminder – those Letters Patent once received from the sovereign herself, 'Whereby our loyal and trusty subject Ronald Knox Mawer shall enjoy all the privileges and courtesies of one of Our Judges of Our High Court'.

In my fury I took a step backwards.

This was a fatal mistake.

I felt my heel slip upon a large piece of orange peel. The next second I was on the floor amidst a heap of papers and Stone's *Justices Manual*, Volumes One and Two.

'May I take it that your submission is at an end?' enquired Mrs Brandock with a crocodile smile.

Recovering myself I tried to pull my case together, but it was too late.

In view of his sensational criminal record I suppose it was hardly surprising that bail was refused. Kevin was nonchalant over the result, unlike his family who gathered in a menacing claque in the doorway to see me off.

'Pissing awful,' said an elder brother.

'Call yourself a barrister?' demanded his mother.

'Usher says he's been abroad for donkey's years,' one of the sisters added.

Grandma's cracked voice followed me as I retreated down the steps. 'Pity they didn't keep him there,' was her final verdict on my performance.

A Case of Bananas

Reviewing my prospects on the journey back to Liverpool, it was evident I was going to have an uphill struggle to make my mark at the Bar. How could I expect a flow of solicitors' briefs with this kind of result?

Back in Oriel Chambers a letter was awaiting me from Aunt Sylvia.

'Have you got in touch with your Uncle Reginald?' she wanted to know. 'He might put some work your way.'

Uncle Reggie! I had assumed that my elderly solicitor uncle had long ago passed on to the Wills and Probate section of the Afterlife.

An enquiry with the operator gave me his home number in Doncaster.

A housekeeper answered.

'Yes,' she reported, 'the old gentleman would like to see his nephew.'

I was on the next train.

Chapter Nineteen

Legal Aid for Mice

I FOUND poor Uncle Reggie in extremely frail health. The housekeeper showed me up to his bedroom. He was propped against a bolster surrounded by all manner of parchments.

'Gave up going to the office twenty years ago,' he told me. 'Devoted myself to antiquarian studies. Early canon law is my special field.'

Through his ear-trumpet I explained my own situation.

'Perhaps you're not cut out for the rough and tumble of advocacy, my boy,' he quavered. 'Why not try for some academic job? You'd enjoy doing legal research, I'm sure – this sort of thing, for instance.' He shuffled among the papers on the bed. I caught a glimpse of various learned journals – *Transactions of the Society of Ecclesiastical Jurists* and *Medieval Jurisprudence*, for instance. There were one or two pieces under Uncle Reginald's own name – *Some Sidelights on the Trial of Cranmer* was one.

'Come over and see me and we'll try and work on something a bit off the beaten track,' were his parting words.

It was not, alas, to be. Three months later the name of Reginald Payne-Toxeter, Lawyer and Antiquarian, appeared in the deaths column of the *Telegraph*. By his will I received a legacy of £250 and a file entitled, 'The Prosecution of Natural Species under Early Canon Law'. Perhaps this explained why he had left the rest of his money towards 'the protection of wild life in forest, wood and stream'!

As I began to read I could understand Uncle Reggie's latest concern. What he had done was to unearth some extraordinary legal records which demonstrated that, in the fourteenth-century clerical world, the instinctive behaviour of the lower forms of creation merited criminal prosecution. Such cases had been dealt with by the Church courts which were so powerful at that time.

It was hard to believe, yet apparently the ecclesiastical law regarded every creature, great and small, as answerable for his or her behaviour. Uncle Reginald seemed to have concentrated on smaller animals. There, on the opening page of R. Payne-Toxeter's draft manuscript, was reproduced a consistory record from York Minster in 1395. An indictment was quoted concerning 'an assemblie of mice'. The mice were charged for 'wantonly eating ye barley crop in ye hundred of Ashby, Lincoln'. It transpired (according to the seventeenth-century translations upon which Uncle Reggie – and later, myself – relied) that the culprits had been ordered to appear on the first day of Lenten Term. One Richard Chamberlain was appointed by Bishop Rewell to plead on behalf of the mice.

'Perhaps the very first example of free legal representation,' Uncle R. Payne-Toxeter observed in a footnote.

Master Chamberlain had taken, as his opening objection, the fact that his clients were dispersed over a large tract of country. 'They dwelle', the clerk had recorded 'in numerous holles. Therefore ye single summons be insufficient in Canon Law to notify ye mice.' Instead, therefore, the President of the court ordered details of the offence to be published from the pulpits of all the parishes in the county.

There was a curious gap here. It seemed that a year had elapsed. Not surprisingly, when the case came up again, there was still no sign of the felonious mice. Mr Chamberlain was required to explain. He was obviously an ingenious defence advocate. He cited an earlier ecclesiastical authority that 'if when journeying to courte ye defendant be placed in perile, attendance thereat be excusable'. The peril to which counsel referred was clear. 'Ye mice', he pointed out, 'muste be eternally vigilant for ye slightest movement of ye cattes.'

Another adjournment was permitted. Eventually, just seven mice were trapped and brought before the court in a basket. Testimony was adduced against them. Judgment was duly read. Six of the mice – one being acquitted on a technicality – received 'ye sentence of anathema accompanied by solemne chantying and the ringinge of ye grate belle'.

My case-hardened lawyer's heart was touched at once. I pictured the whole drama in a series of Beatrix Potter drawings. How had such injustices been allowed? In my mind's eye stood a row of troubled mice holding up their mittened paws for mercy, while their colleagues were led below in tiny chains.

Like Uncle Reggie, I was hooked at once to the whole bizarre subject which he had obviously hoped I would pursue. Upon an impulse I took the train to York. There, in the Consistory Archives, I was soon immersed in dusty volumes and faded scrolls. For the next six weeks my current briefs lay forgotten on my desk in Liverpool. Even a promising *cause célèbre*, the matrimonial troubles of Mrs Greasby of 9 Derby Villas, Everton, were forgotten while I investigated these miniature miscarriages of justice.

A Case of Bananas

As for insects, they enjoyed no amnesty at all. I discovered, for instance, a court-roll involving the prosecution of gnats by the parishioners of Thoresby. The source of complaint in that instance was 'ye swallowing of ye gnats by suche as are of tender yeres'.

The Thoresby attorney had pointed out that, in considering the question, account should be taken of five classes of sinful inclination on the part of gnats: self preservation, wanton destructiveness, vanity, egotism and covetousness. Moreover, he asserted, since the devil could take the shape of any creature, a careless child in swallowing a gnat might swallow the Prince of Darkness himself. Malediction and perpetual banishment seemed inevitable as far as the gnats were concerned.

Counsel had been assigned – legal aid again – to defend the gnats. His name was William Beaumont, and the hearing was held before Abbot John Barkworth. Mr Beaumont argued that his clients were all part of the divine order of things and entitled to an undisturbed place in that order.

The prosecutor, Richard Eddystone, countered this submission by reference to Holy Writ. The scriptures, he urged, bore no record of a pair of gnats having been taken by Noah 'into ye arke'.

This seemed to have persuaded the President of the court, Abbot Barkworth, to excommunicate the gnats. A solemn *de excommunicatione insectorum* was pronounced and duly recorded.

Returning to my seat in the deserted Consistory Archives I found that a helpful clerk had laid more documents for me to see. I was following up another note by Uncle Reggie in the margin; this simply said 'Moles'/438. Sure enough there was a record of a family of moles being brought to trial. According to the princi-

al witness, the bailiff working for Lord de Clifford, 'ye
moles had churned up ye courtyard of ye residence of
mye lorde'.

One Dr Mortimer was briefed to defend the moles. He
insisted that his clients, far from being blameworthy,
did in fact improve Lord de Clifford's land, 'by throw-
nge up ye soile they do enrich ye said tenement'.

This averment did not help the moles. A formal malediction was declared upon them. 'Ye are banned from
his Province of Canterbury under penaltie of eternale
damnatione,' they were told. It is not recorded whether
he moles accepted this dread pronouncement or
appealed directly to Rome.

Burrowing elsewhere, in other cathedral archives
under the cloisters, I began to feel like one of the moles.
Although I must admit that, in Chester for instance, I
found it difficult to summon up quite the same degree of
sympathy for termites. Even so, I decided there was no
excusing the ecclesiastical court which sat in 1452 with
Chancellor Hugh Taplin presiding, to hear a complaint
against an unspecified number of termites. They had
done, it was said, 'wanton damage to ye Churche
Recordes'. According to the evidence on the Roll a
lengthy discussion had ensued as to whether, since the
termites inhabited what had always been regarded as
hallowed ground (the close of Chester Cathedral), they
were entitled to plead 'benefit of clergy'. Or were they
laity? Chancellor Taplin ruled that the burden of proof,
that the termites were entitled to benefit of clergy, lay
upon the insects themselves. Otherwise, he decided,
they must be presumed to be laity. Since, as the
seventeenth-century translation explained, it was 'not
certaine that ye subjectes of ye indictement were visible
to ye court', it was unlikely that they were in a position
to discharge this burden of proof. As a consequence the

termites were declared Doomed in Perpetuity.

In all these investigations, Uncle Reggie was my invaluable guide. At page seventeen of his uncompleted treatise he referred to a trial of 'ye pest of flyes' held before Archdeacon Richard Ravenser of St Albans in 1449. The Archdeacon's ruling is given as follows: 'In consyderatione of ye smalle syze of ye flyes, none of same havinge rechede mejoretie, ye flyes shall retyre without anathema to ye common lande.'

The earliest medieval case which I could find was a citation from the Abbey Court of Glastonbury (c. 1350). This was a prosecution against a family of cockroaches for having caused 'grate distructione to ye oates collected in ye barnes'. Abbot Selby accepted a plea of guilty entered on behalf of the cockroaches by their counsel, Henry Galliere. Incense was lit and the Abbot addressed the offenders in stern tones. 'Thou irrationale and imperfect cretures,' he declared, 'ye are forever accursed.'

Towards the end of his notes Uncle Payne-Toxeter listed several warrants issued by Abbot Richard de Sleford in Alnwick before 1333 and 1337. Upon the complaint of the Prior of Morpeth against 'certain mothes for having damaged ye vestments', the moths were ordered to 'severallie pleade, demur, or replie that ye warrante may not be ratifiede'. Another warrant was issued for the interdiction of 'ye plague of midges', but no outcome of this suit was mentioned. Unlike the case of the sparrows.

In 1381, Prior Thomas Stoyll of Warter Priory sought advice from Rome in respect of a prosecution of sparrows for 'makying too free with ye milk from ye cowes'. In his dispatch the Prior pointed out that 'ye sparrows are more easily accursed than man in that ye spirit of man resists more than that of ye brute'. Pope Nicholas

IV obviously had a soft spot for sparrows. He advised that the bolt of excommunication should not be hurled recklessly against these creatures since 'if it faileth in its objecte it returneth and smiteth hym that hath hurled itt'. The Prior took this advice to heart and a subsequent entry in the accounts of the Priory was to the effect: 'Payd Robt Hammond for driving sparrowes out of Priorye, one groate.'

I had garnered enough material to complete Uncle Reggie's manuscript. Perhaps one day I would be able to publish it under our joint names. That would have pleased the old boy and would maybe give me a foothold in the world of legal research. Meanwhile, it was time to return to my small flat in Liverpool.

Upon the kitchen table there was a note from Mildred, the cleaning lady.

'Dear Mr Knox,' it read, 'a mouse has been eating your creamcrackers. So have set trap. Good luck – Mildred.'

With a sinking heart I opened the cupboard-door. There, among the last crumbs of the Crawford's packet, was a hole in the wall and, nearby, the ready-sprung device. Carefully, I deposited it in the rubbish-bin. No species of animal life, however unruly its behaviour, was to receive an arbitrary capital-sentence in my establishment.

Next morning I hurried along to Woolworths. A liberal insertion of Polyfilla into the intruder's front door would unquestionably be preferable – even to excommunication – for any God-fearing mouse.

Moreover, under current government limits, this would solve the esoteric problems over the granting of free legal aid for mice.

Chapter Twenty

Back to Square One

IT WAS NOT SURPRISING that, after my anti-quarian investigations into the protection of wildlife, I should find myself remembering Mr Pandit Raj Sharma, since the religious outlook of my former Court Registrar carried this principle to extremes.

For example, when a swarm of locusts had descended on my vegetable garden, which I was trying to cultivate, at the Judges' Lodging, Marbala, he firmly stopped my efforts to eliminate them.

'All life must be nurtured,' he declared, reprimanding me through the shutters as the pestilential creatures demolished my carefully tended row of spinach. 'Nothing must be destroyed. Such is the will of the Great Divine Power.'

There was also the unforgettable occasion on the Nambatu Assize Circuit when my sitting was made insufferable by a plague of Samoan pinewasps. Their bite was far more painful than the mosquito, producing unsightly weals on both my face and neck.

'The use of Government-issue pesticide is out of the question,' the Registrar decreed. 'They enjoy a universal right of survival under Lord Krishna's edict. They must live as we must live.'

'This is ridiculous,' I said, as another of the wretched

168

creatures zoomed across the Bench, targeting on my left ear. The Registrar's response was to present me with a Polynesian feathered-reed fan as used by the lady dancers of Nambatu. 'This should keep the wasps at bay,' he insisted.

But it was wholly inappropriate for me to wave a bright pink plume from side to side while handing out a deterrent sentence for what the Nambatu Island Ordinance classified as a serious felony: 'Flirting on the Sabbath in a Public Place.'

Finally, Mr Sharma agreed that I could try another method of thwarting my tormentors. I reached into my travelling library-box and brought out The Big Red Book. Needless to say, the Army and Navy Stores catalogue advertised a complete service for tropical insect protection. One item on offer comprised an elaborate kind of veil. Indeed, the illustration in the BRB looked like my own father dressed for bee-keeping.

Another cheaper piece of equipment was a steel-mesh affair more like an old-fashioned meat-safe. Mr Sharma naturally plumped for the less expensive item. He was inflexible over cutting down official expenditure.

'But surely,' I protested, 'that one's for out-of-doors work. On plantations and so forth?'

'Perfectly suitable,' was his reply. 'And a big saving on the Court budget.'

Unfortunately, this Mark 2 protector simply had the effect of transforming me into a Man in the Iron Mask. Nevertheless, Mr Sharma only consented to change his ruling when a jury complained that the equipment made me inaudible.

'And why does the judge need such a thing,' the foreman had complained belligerently, 'when Government gives us members of the jury no protection against bites?'

169

A Case of Bananas

In vain Mr Sharma explained that the wasps were drawn to foreign blood from cooler climes and the judge's own thin skin made him particularly vulnerable.

In due course he sanctioned a more expensive item which became part of my court regalia whenever occasion demanded. Yet there was a certain luxury about the light gauziness of the protector – worn suspended from my wig – which aroused Mr Sharma's latent disapproval. He believed that plagues of all sorts were sent to teach man powers of endurance. Life for the human race, he said, was not meant to be pleasant. Forbearance in the face of vicissitude was required. It was a quaint contradiction to the indulgence he afforded lower forms of life. Human transgression, in Mr Sharma's view, must be punished stringently. 'Far too lenient,' was his repeated complaint over my sentencing policy.

Upon one occasion, after a raid on Chung Yee's Peanut Shop, I put two village youths on a Community Service Order. Mr Sharma clicked his tongue in disapproval. They were daredevil sixteen-year-olds in fluorescent teeshirts with the slogan 'Power Now', emblazoned on the front.

As part of their community work I instructed them to service the court limousine. Regrettably, when they'd finished with the car – a pre-war Morris Cowley – I had to admit it was the worse for wear. I managed to cope with the maladjustment of the steering column but, as Mr Sharma pointed out, they had completely removed certain vital parts of the machine. In particular, they had dismantled the exhaust system. This was all too evident when my arrival at court was punctuated by a series of loud explosions.

'Everybody take cover,' bellowed Josefa, my Police Orderly, from the front steps. The offenders had also

removed the brake linings which was why I was unable
to slow down. Fortunately, the strength of the chassis
and the width of the running-board stopped the vehicle
halfway through the dock and everybody managed to
get safely clear.

'If only your honour had listened to me,' reprimanded
Mr Sharma. It was a favourite remark. Listening to
sound advice was a vital axiom. Whatever one's station
in life some people were pupils and some were teachers.
It was not difficult to know into which categories Mr
Sharma and I had been placed.

Now back in England for good, I was free at last from
Mr Sharma's shadow and his maddening insistence
upon running my life from dawn to dusk.

I had enjoyed my foray into medieval canon law but,
back in Oriel Chambers, I was gradually building a
modest practice in the lower echelons of the Northern
Circuit – but hoping for more promising work. Requests
for my services were always handled by Mr Briggs and,
after an especially prolonged session on the telephone,
he came in to me with a twinkle in his eye.

'Are you available during the August holiday?' he
inquired.

'I've no intention of taking time off,' I said. 'But if it's
another Magistrates Court appearance for that
Huchisson Street gang,' I said, 'tell them I've had
enough of their thieving ways.'

'I don't think stealing lead from derelict church roofs
is quite the Lord Chancellor's line,' replied the Chief
Clerk.

'The Lord Chancellor?!'

'Yes, his office wants to know if you'll sit as a Deputy
Floating Judge at London Sessions.' I put down my pen.

'They're desperately looking for someone with experience on the Bench and want to know if you'll stand in as a judge there,' said Mr Briggs. 'Their original replacement has let them down. Most people are not available at that time of year, especially now London's having the worst heatwave in history. Lucky you're used to that kind of thing.'

I nodded uncertainly.

'Anyway,' continued the Chief Clerk, 'you're to report as soon as possible to the Assistant Comptroller of Sessions at Bush House in the Strand. He'll show you the ropes and so on.'

I made my preparations that weekend. At least my credentials had been spotted by the powers that be. It looked as though my career in the UK was ready for take-off.

Of course it was premature to lash out over accommodation, so I booked in with Mrs Giles, my old landlady, in Bernard Street, Russell Square. A notice in front of the faded lace curtains said 'Rooms Available', which was not surprising as the whole of the Victorian terrace was being demolished for an office block.

The scaffolders started work outside my window at 5.30 a.m. next morning. So I was in good time for my appointment at Bush House.

It proved a heady experience crossing the freshly scrubbed marble hall of this great nerve-centre of London judicial administration. A far cry, I thought, from the pitted verandah of Suba Courts Administration HQ.

'The Assistant Comptroller will be with you shortly,' said a secretary in the second-floor suite. 'He's been delayed at a Home Office meeting.' She handed me a coffee cup stamped with the City Coat of Arms. 'I believe you know him already.'

I shook my head. 'Must be mixing me up with

omeone else,' I said. 'I've never worked on the London Bench before.'

The buzz of the intercom interrupted our onversation.

'Deputy Judge Knox Mawer is here, sir,' she said. 'I'll how him in.'

She opened an intervening door marked 'Courts dministration'. As I followed her across the threshold a urious feeling of apprehension overcame me. Now I nderstood why. Seated behind an enormous desk was omeone who bore an uncanny resemblance to the Court Registrar of all my years in the South Pacific.

We meet again,' said Mr Pandit Raj Sharma, advancing o shake my hand with an encouraging smile. 'Small vorld!'

The glasses were thicker, the hair was now entirely rey but the former Registrar's manner was quite nchanged. My tongue went dry. It was like one of those ightmares in which incongruous figures from the past eappear in a new and threatening role.

'Mr Sharma! How on earth did you come to leave the 'acific?' I stammered.

'The old story, I'm afraid. The people were not suf-iciently educated for Independence,' he said in his fam-liar, lecturing tone. 'British justice went out of the vindow and my job with it. So I applied for a similar osition in this country.'

I nodded, mesmerized.

'I had first-class qualifications and a British passport, f course,' he went on, adjusting his cuffs. 'So I went up he ladder pretty quickly.' He placed his spectacles on he end of his nose and peered over them. 'I was never fraid of hard work, you recall. Hard work and iscipline!'

A Case of Bananas

'I remember,' I said feebly, trying to regain some composure.

How could I adjust to the fact that here I was, back in my native capital after a lifetime's service in foreign parts, only to be shackled into duty once again by my old colonial mentor, Pandit Raj Sharma?

As if reading my thoughts he said, 'You'll be feeling like a new boy, I expect.'

He tightened the knot of his tie. It had silver scales of justice embroidered upon it.

'Don't worry. I'm here to set you on the right path.'

I was about to speak but thought better of it.

'Since leaving the Overseas Service I understand you've been off the Bench and back at the Bar.'

He made it sound like a punishment for bad behaviour.

'I've built up quite a decent little practice on the Northern Circuit,' I said defensively.

'Ah yes.' Mr Sharma blew his nose at length, in his familiar fashion. 'I don't want to rule out all chance of promotion for you. But London is very different from the provinces, of course.'

'But much more expensive,' I countered, 'and then there's all the commuting.'

'I'm very fortunate to be living in West Two,' replied Mr Sharma. 'Most spacious accommodation for me and my family off Edgware Road. And extremely convenient for the Temple of Shiva.'

'The Temple of Shiva?' I repeated.

For a moment I was back in the township of Lovasi with the ringing of bells and the chanting of the priestly fire-walkers drifting in from the temple compound next to the court, with the bellowing of Mr Sharma's two sacred cows adding to the hubbub.

The Assistant Comptroller quickly brought me back to

the present. 'We have a very fine shrine just completed off the Marylebone Overpass. You must make a visit some time.'

He cleared his throat and produced a file out of his briefcase. It was headed 'Schedule of Judicial Personnel'.

'I see you're in our reserve section of temporary appointments,' he explained. 'Understandable. A start at least.'

We parted on the steps of Bush House.

'I think I can find the court-house alright,' I said. 'The nearest tube station is Elephant and Castle, isn't it?'

'Quite unnecessary,' said Mr Sharma. 'I'll call for you with George, my official chauffeur.'

Chapter Twenty-One

Palm Court Reversed

'A VERY SMART BLACK CAR waiting for you,' called Mrs Giles through my bedroom door next morning. 'Indian gentleman rang the bell. Ever so well spoken. Said at first he must have got the wrong address.' My heart sank. My bohemian lodgings of student days had obviously earned me another C minus in Mr Sharma's personal scale of marking.

'Good morning, Deputy,' said Mr Sharma, once again emphasizing my substitute-status. His starched white collar gleamed out of the shadows as I joined him on the back seat. I myself was still making do with yesterday's shirt. Mrs Giles had told me firmly that the laundry man only called once a week and, besides, his charges these days were 'something criminal'.

'You were oversleeping, maybe,' chaffed the Assistant Comptroller, as we glided off.

'Not used to the noise of the traffic, I'm afraid,' I mumbled.

Mr Sharma rubbed his hands together vigorously. It was an old habit of his, intended to emphasize the alertness of one who was invariably up betimes.

'You should study the International Yoga Technique for Awakening the Mind and Body.'

I remembered Mr Sharma's enthusiasm for this par-

icular exercise in self-improvement. He had once given
me a large quantity of brightly coloured hand-printed
leaflets on the subject. No doubt these still lay in my
Army and Navy Stores Globetrotter cabin-trunk where
they had proved invaluable for wrapping up china and
glass.

'London Sessions please, George,' said the ACS to the
chauffeur. We were diverted into St James's where it
was obvious that the refuse collectors were on strike
again. Mr Sharma frowned out of the window at the
mountain of black bags. 'Litter everywhere,' he observed. He raised his silk scarf over his nose and mouth
as we became locked in a traffic-jam and petrol fumes
seeped through the windows. I caught a litany of muffled complaints as the steel-rimmed spectacles flashed
critically from side to side.

'Western pollution, acid rain, population explosion,
inner-city decay!' He pointed a censorious finger at
Nelson's Column which was covered in scaffolding.

'Whole place is going to rack and ruin. Even the
venerable statues of our great heroes!'

A group of girls in mini-skirts were posing by the
Landseer lions.

Mr Sharma peered out more closely.

'Highly immoral spectacle,' he observed. 'Never
allowed in good caste society.'

We drew up at London Sessions House.

'Morning, sir,' called the police sergeant on duty at
the entrance. He saluted Mr Sharma, nodding at me as
an afterthought.

'Does he have a pass, sir?'

'He's with me,' the ACS assured him.

A uniformed official scurried forward with a sheaf of
papers under his arm.

'Tell the Presiding Judge I'll be along to see him in a

few minutes,' said the ACS.

He led the way through a series of imposing corridors, pausing only to flick away a speck of dust from the bronze plaque commemorating the opening of the building.

'Cleaning ladies getting slack again.'

I followed him through some swing-doors.

'Your chambers are this way,' he said. 'In the Annexe.'

We crossed the compound, entered a side street and passed a launderette where we forked right over some waste-ground used for breaking up old cars. Skirting a heap of disused tyres he indicated a prefabricated hut attached to a sooty building of Victorian brick.

Somebody had stuck up a handwritten sign, 'Deputy Judge Nox More', on a cracked pane of glass. Inside was a plasterboard cell with a solitary desk and chair on a peeling red lino floor.

'This,' said Mr Sharma, 'is your Retiring Room.'

The suffocating heat reminded me forcibly of the barren, phosphate island of Nauru astride the equator, to which I had once paid a short and dreadful visit when serving in the Pacific.

Mr Sharma must have seen my jaw fall.

'I'm afraid only permanent judges have accommodation in the main building,' he said.

He laid a sympathetic hand on my shoulder.

I felt that odd tweak of affection that had always underlain my relationship with Mr Sharma, however exasperating the circumstances.

'Remember, you are expert at making the best of rough-and-ready situations,' he reminded me.

I had pulled out my gown from its bag and, almost out of habit, Mr Sharma helped me on with it.

'At least it's no worse than the old court-house on the bench at Lovaka,' he reminisced, 'where the roof was falling in and there was a smell of stale fish from the market on the back verandah. You couldn't hear yourself speak with all that hammering from the boatyard next door.'

I was finding it difficult to hear Mr Sharma speak above the growing cacophony of sound from outside my London seat of justice. There was a loud squeal of brakes and, through the slat in the window, I could see the Brixton Prison van backing up with its load of detainees. A shrill female voice – obviously one of the jury in waiting – complained to the Jury Bailiff of the absence of a ladies' convenience.

'There's a Portaloo just behind the warrant-office, madam,' he replied in a stentorian tone.

From over the wire fence I caught the jingle of an ice-cream bell. 'Lovely cornets. Chocolate or vanilla.'

A very young clerk came bounding in to the room with an armful of files.

'This is Keith,' said Mr Sharma.

The ginger-headed youth gave a toothy smile, then turned to the ACS. 'Only odds and sods this morning, sir.' I gathered he was referring to my Cause List. The ACS nodded, rustling through the papers.

'Should do nicely for the Deputy Judge,' he said. 'Give him chance to get the hang of things.'

'Tracey,' called Keith. 'Some typing for you.'

A blonde girl in excessively high-heels teetered in and took a sheet of paper from Keith.

'See you later, alligator,' quipped Keith as Tracey shimmied out again.

'In a while, crocodile,' came the pert reply.

Mr Sharma clicked his tongue.

'Those swinging sixties!' he snapped. 'What have the young people done to the language of Shakespeare! All because of a great decline in our British educational system.'

179

A Case of Bananas

He checked the clock with his wristwatch, an ornate Japanese affair, showing the phases of the sun and moon as well as the day and week. 'Half a minute out,' he scolded, before hurrying off to more important business.

It was time to move into the adjoining court-building.

'Disused chapel,' explained Keith, leading me through a small back door. After mounting five curved wooden steps I found myself perched under a gothic canopy of polished oak. The jury was already seated in the largest of the box-pews. Counsel and solicitors occupied the front of the nave, with the public jammed in an old gallery at the back.

'All mod cons,' said Keith.

He pulled a cord over my head. The fluorescent strip flickered on, then off again.

'What's that noise?' I asked nervously. An eerie whistling sound seemed to be coming from behind me.

'It's the draught from the organ pipes,' whispered Keith. 'Can't do nothing about it.'

He took his place on a stool at the lectern and handed up the charge-sheets.

The cases themselves were as curious as the Alice-in-Wonderland setting. Three defendants popped up in quick succession behind the bronze rail of what had once been the deacon's stall.

In a kind of trance I placed an eighty-four-year-old vicar (defrocked) on probation, for persistent bigamy, bound over a lady wrestler who had given her landlord a black eye for sexual harassment, and fined a Japanese tourist for sunbathing in the nude on Tower Bridge.

It was now midday and time for the main trial to begin.

'Bring up Arthur Fowler,' called Keith into what had

180

once been the boiler-room.

There was the sound of booted feet below and the clanging of doors. As we waited, the court-room provided its own distractions. A drunk had already been evicted from the back row, with much smashing of bottles. Now the Duty Officer was in the process of removing a large bearded man who was waving a placard at me with the mysterious slogan, FIDEL CASTRO RULES O.K. I could not help reflecting that the simple islanders of Polynesia showed more respect for the Bench. To add to my discomfort, I seemed to have a cold coming on.

'Sorry about all this,' said Keith in an undertone. 'It's always the same in a heatwave.'

I banged the paper-weight on the pulpit in front of me.

'Could we please have silence,' I croaked.

A ferret-faced man in a check muffler had surfaced in the dock alongside the jailer. Consulting the register, headed Larceny, I felt on more familiar ground. The prisoner, a jobbing builder from Peckham, was charged with a continuous series of thefts. He had removed the floorboards from a row of terraced houses in Southwark, claiming that the property had been abandoned and was there for the taking. His furtive manner did not inspire confidence in his honesty. I made a careful note of counsel's cross-examination but found it hard to concentrate. A violent headache had started up around the eyes. It was not just my cold. The stuffy, dust-laden atmosphere of the place had already brought on my old sinusitis.

I was making discreet use of my pocket nasal-inhaler when I became aware of more scuffling in the public section. Suddenly a shrill cry went up.

'That Judge! He's not fit to try my husband. He's an addick!'

A Case of Bananas

A police constable moved towards the heckler, a heavily made-up lady with a peroxide hair-do and long, *diamanté* earrings.

'Anyone can see what he's up to. Sniffing glue. Calm as you like. Just like the ones on the telly.'

Alongside her, a remarkably similar lady – related, no doubt – was also on her feet.

'More likely it's coke. Just look at his horrible white face. Been on drugs for years, if you ask me.'

'I really must protest, madam,' I began. 'These grotesque allegations . . .' But before I could continue, both women had been removed – defiantly waving their handbags.

In my confusion I failed to notice a reporter from the Press Box slip out behind them.

'Sorry, your honour,' apologized the Court Officer. 'That was Mrs Fowler and her sister. Watching too many of them "Panorama" programmes, I shouldn't wonder.'

The foreman of the jury stood up.

'Permission to speak, sir,' he said. He was an earnest stooping man. 'We want to assure his honour of our support.'

There was a murmur of approval from his colleagues.

'We hear he's seen service abroad. Speaking for myself, I was stationed with the RAF in Singapore and my health's never been the same since.'

He was about to enlarge on this theme when I held up my hand.

'Thank you, Mr Foreman,' I said. 'Most appreciated. However, the case is adjourned until tomorrow.'

'Court rise,' called Keith.

Collecting my papers I hurried out and crossed over to the Annexe. I was glad to gather myself together in the sanctuary of the Retiring Room. The prison van had departed and all was peace and quiet again.

Bringing out Mrs Giles's thermos and sandwiches, I spent the afternoon transcribing my notes and consulting the latest edition of Archbold's *Pleading, Evidence and Practice in Criminal Cases*, edited by T.R. Fitzwalter Butler.

I was making preparations to leave when Keith brought in a copy of the London *Evening Standard*.

'Final edition,' he said in jocular fashion. 'All the latest.'

Then, more soberly, he turned up an inside page.

'Disturbance at London Sessions', read a column. They had somehow got hold of a photograph of me – from the files at the Commonwealth Office no doubt. It showed me inspecting the Guard of Honour at the height of the Hot Season in Tulalau, after a nasty bout of gippy-tummy. I certainly looked like a man on his last legs. Beneath the photograph was an account of the morning's incident and the ludicrous abuse of me by Mrs Fowler and her sister, in full verbatim.

'The ACS would be happy to see you in Bush House at your convenience, after court tomorrow,' Keith added, leaving the paper on my desk for further study.

Chapter Twenty-Two

Envoi

NEXT DAY I reconvened the court and completed the Fowler trial without further interruption. The jury acquitted upon all counts.

In the office a tactful silence was maintained about the newspaper report. But the thought of my forthcoming encounter with Mr Sharma weighed on my mind.

The ACS was giving me lunch at a fashionable Indian restaurant off the Strand. He was studying the menu with a frown of concentration when I arrived. Ordering for us both, he tucked a napkin into his waistcoat and gave me his attention.

'A highly unfortunate incident,' he pronounced.

'It all had to do with a stupid misunderstanding . . .' I began.

'The press seizes on anything that makes a mock of the Bench, of course,' he said, blowing his nose majestically. 'The Comptroller was at a loss to understand how it could have happened in the first place.'

I tried again. 'My sinuses were giving a lot of trouble, you see, and I had to use my inhaler.'

'Inhaler?' Mr Sharma repeated doubtfully.

He tapped his fingers on the table and looked around impatiently. 'Lazy people these Bangladeshi waiters,' he complained. 'Should be sent back to their own

184

country. See how they like that.'

He held up his glass to the light and polished it with his handkerchief. The sound of a zitar and a deep-throated female warbling flooded out from the loud-speaker above our heads.

Furiously, Mr Sharma beckoned to the manager.

'Have this music turned off at once. Very lowest kind of Indian film-music. And we are still waiting for our food.' It arrived as he spoke, and the next half hour was devoted to its consumption.

The dhal was pronounced 'almost cold' but the prawn vindaloo seemed up to standard. He drained two glasses of water in quick succession, then sat back and studied me over his spectacles.

'Let us put that particular incident behind us,' he said, 'although I have to tell you that the Comptroller and I have had a chat about your career in general terms. Your health, for example.'

'I always give of my best,' I asserted.

'These metropolitan courts!' said Mr Sharma. He shook his head. 'It is like trying to keep law and order in the Amazonian jungle. The judge needs to be in tip-top condition. He must have nerves of steel and an iron constitution.'

He raised his eyebrows.

'London's underworld does not respect a sensitive temperament such as yours, maybe.'

I brought out a tissue and mopped away my tears – the result of a rashly ordered dish of chillies.

Mr Sharma leaned over and patted my head.

'No need to take it to heart,' he said. 'When one door closes, another one opens.'

Six months later, Mr Sharma forwarded my delayed claim for travelling expenses. '£12.2s.6d.' he had dock-eted in magenta ink. Attached to the document was a letter in his own hand.

A Case of Bananas

Your request for the enclosed suggests that fees are in short supply in these cut-back days for barristers. I am truly concerned for your future in the UK. My family has a proposal to make. My brother-in-law is expanding his travel business and is setting up Paradise Cruisers Limited to tour the South Pacific. He is needing a lecturer on board to commentate on the islands for the benefit of the passengers. It strikes me how well suited you would be in this role with your knowledge of the South Seas. Americans would be specially pleased to have a pillar of the old British Empire like yourself with them. The post is yours for the asking. So why not be thinking it over?

Meanwhile, drop a line to my brother-in-law himself, Mr Roy Handa, Handa House, Handa Road, Bombay.

I put down the letter and gazed out of my window at Oriel Chambers. Sleet was falling over the Gladstone Dock.

Perhaps I should consider Mr Sharma's proposal seriously. Deep down I felt the old wanderlust stir again. It could be that I was, by nature, a rolling stone destined to gather no moss. At least my expertise on Polynesian culture would be put to fruitful use.

My gaberdine raincoat was steaming gently over the radiator. It struck me that, if I accepted the invitation, I would have to re-equip myself for tropical climes right from scratch.

In the corner of the room stood my Globetrotter safari trunk, now used for storing legal books. Also in there was a volume of much more vital importance.

I reached in and cast aside Halsbury's *Laws of England*. There, in the bottom, was what I was looking for – my original copy of The Big Red Book.